The
Econo

Pocket
World in
Figures

2009 Concise Edition

Contents

Notes for the full edition

This 2009 edition of *The Economist Pocket World in Figures*
includes new rankings on such things as privacy, gold
reserves, student performance, teenagers' behaviour, obesity,
mortgage debt, Oscars, press freedom, death row, slums and
various environmental measures. The world rankings consider
186 countries; all those with a population of at least 1m or a
GDP of at least $1bn. The country profiles cover 67 major
countries. Also included are profiles of the euro area and the
world. The extent and quality of the statistics available varies
from country to country. Every care has been taken to specify
the broad definitions on which the data are based and to
indicate cases where data quality or technical difficulties are
such that interpretation of the figures is likely to be seriously
affected. Nevertheless, figures from individual countries may
differ from standard international statistical definitions. The
term "country" can also refer to territories or economic
entities.

Some country definitions
Macedonia is officially known as the Former Yugoslav Republic
of Macedonia. Data for Cyprus normally refer to Greek Cyprus
only. Data for China do not include Hong Kong or Macau. For
countries such as Morocco they exclude disputed areas.
Congo-Kinshasa refers to the Democratic Republic of Congo,
formerly known as Zaire. Congo-Brazzaville refers to the other
Congo. Data for the EU refer to the 25 members prior to the
addition of Bulgaria and Romania on January 1 2007, unless
otherwise noted. Euro area data normally refer to the 12
members that had adopted the euro as at December 31 2006:
Austria, Belgium, France, Finland, Germany, Greece, Ireland,
Italy, Luxembourg, Netherlands, Portugal and Spain.

Statistical basis
The all-important factor in a book of this kind is to be able to
make reliable comparisons between countries. Although this
is never quite possible for the reasons stated above, the best
route, which this book takes, is to compare data for the same
year or period and to use actual, not estimated, figures
wherever possible. Where a country's data is excessively out of
date, it is excluded. The research for this edition of *The
Economist Pocket World in Figures* was carried out in 2008
using the latest available sources that present data on an
internationally comparable basis.
    Data in the country profiles, unless otherwise indicated,

refer to the year ending December 31 2006. Life expectancy , crude birth, death and fertility rates are based on 2005–10 averages; human development indices and energy data are for 2005; marriage and divorce data refer to the latest year for which figures are available. Employment, health and education data are for the latest year between 2000 and 2006.

Other definitions
Data shown in country profiles may not always be consistent with those shown in the world rankings because the definitions or years covered can differ.

Statistics for principal exports and principal imports are normally based on customs statistics. These are generally compiled on different definitions to the visible exports and imports figures shown in the balance of payments section.

Definitions of the statistics shown are given on the relevant page or in the glossary. Figures may not add exactly to totals, or percentages to 100, because of rounding or, in the case of GDP, statistical adjustment. Sums of money have generally been converted to US dollars at the official exchange rate ruling at the time to which the figures refer.

Energy consumption data are not always reliable, particularly for the major oil producing countries; consumption per head data may therefore be higher than in reality. Energy exports can exceed production and imports can exceed consumption if transit operations distort trade data or oil is imported for refining and re-exported.

Abbreviations

bn	billion (one thousand million)	m	million
EU	European Union	PPP	Purchasing power parity
kg	kilogram	TOE	tonnes of oil equivalent
km	kilometre	trn	trillion (one thousand billion)
GDP	Gross domestic product	...	not available
ha	hectare		

Countries: natural facts

Countries: *the largest*[a]

'000 sq km

1	Russia	17,075		31	Tanzania	945
2	Canada	9,971		32	Nigeria	924
3	China	9,561		33	Venezuela	912
4	United States	9,373		34	Namibia	824
5	Brazil	8,512		35	Pakistan	804
6	Australia	7,682		36	Mozambique	799
7	India	3,287		37	Turkey	779
8	Argentina	2,767		38	Chile	757
9	Kazakhstan	2,717		39	Zambia	753
10	Sudan	2,506		40	Myanmar	677
11	Algeria	2,382		41	Afghanistan	652
12	Congo	2,345		42	Somalia	638
13	Saudi Arabia	2,200		43	Central African Rep	622
14	Greenland	2,176		44	Ukraine	604
15	Mexico	1,973		45	Madagascar	587
16	Indonesia	1,904		46	Kenya	583
17	Libya	1,760		47	Botswana	581
18	Iran	1,648		48	France	544
19	Mongolia	1,565		49	Yemen	528
20	Peru	1,285		50	Thailand	513
21	Chad	1,284		51	Spain	505
22	Niger	1,267		52	Turkmenistan	488
23	Angola	1,247		53	Cameroon	475
24	Mali	1,240		54	Papua New Guinea	463
25	South Africa	1,226		55	Sweden	450
26	Colombia	1,142		56	Morocco	447
27	Ethiopia	1,134			Uzbekistan	447
28	Bolivia	1,099		58	Iraq	438
29	Mauritania	1,031		59	Paraguay	407
30	Egypt	1,000		60	Zimbabwe	391

Mountains: *the highest*[b]

	Name	Location	Height (m)
1	Everest	Nepal-China	8,848
2	K2 (Godwin Austen)	Pakistan	8,611
3	Kangchenjunga	Nepal-Sikkim	8,586
4	Lhotse	Nepal-China	8,516
5	Makalu	Nepal-China	8,463
6	Cho Oyu	Nepal-China	8,201
7	Dhaulagiri	Nepal	8,167
8	Manaslu	Nepal	8,163
9	Nanga Parbat	Pakistan	8,125
10	Annapurna I	Nepal	8,091
11	Gasherbrum I	Pakistan-China	8,068
12	Broad Peak	Pakistan-China	8,047
13	Xixabangma (Gosainthan)	China	8,046
14	Gasherbrum II	Pakistan-China	8,035

a Includes freshwater.
b Includes separate peaks which are part of the same massif.

Rivers: *the longest*

Name	Location	Length (km)
1 Nile	Africa	6,695
2 Amazon	South America	6,516
3 Yangtze	Asia	6,380
4 Mississippi-Missouri system	North America	6,019
5 Ob'-Irtysh	Asia	5,570
6 Yenisey-Angara	Asia	5,550
7 Hwang He (Yellow)	Asia	5,464
8 Congo	Africa	4,667
9 Parana	South America	4,500
10 Mekong	Asia	4,425

Deserts: *the largest*

Name	Location	Area ('000 sq km)
1 Sahara	Northern Africa	8,600
2 Arabia	SW Asia	2,300
3 Gobi	Mongolia/China	1,166
4 Patagonian	Argentina	673
5 Great Victoria	W and S Australia	647
6 Great Basin	SW United States	492
7 Chihuahuan	N Mexico	450
8 Great Sandy	W Australia	400

Lakes: *the largest*

Name	Location	Area ('000 sq km)
1 Caspian Sea	Central Asia	371
2 Superior	Canada/US	82
3 Victoria	E Africa	69
4 Huron	Canada/US	60
5 Michigan	US	58
6 Tanganyika	E Africa	33
7 Baikal	Russia	32
8 Great Bear	Canada	31

Islands: *the largest*

Name	Location	Area ('000 sq km)
1 Greenland	North Atlantic Ocean	2,176
2 New Guinea	South-west Pacific Ocean	809
3 Borneo	Western Pacific Ocean	746
4 Madagascar	Indian Ocean	587
5 Baffin	North Atlantic Ocean	507
6 Sumatra	North-east Indian Ocean	474
7 Honshu	Sea of Japan-Pacific Ocean	227
8 Great Britain	Off coast of north-west Europe	218

Notes: Estimates of the lengths of rivers vary widely depending on eg, the path to take through a delta. The definition of a desert is normally a mean annual precipitation value equal to 250ml or less. Australia (7.69 sq km) is defined as a continent rather than an island.

Population: size and growth

Largest populations
Millions, 2006

1	China	1,323.6		34	Kenya	35.1
2	India	1,119.5		35	Algeria	33.4
3	United States	301.0		36	Canada	32.6
4	Indonesia	225.5		37	Morocco	31.9
5	Brazil	188.9		38	Afghanistan	31.1
6	Pakistan	161.2		39	Uganda	29.9
7	Bangladesh	144.4		40	Iraq	29.6
8	Russia	142.5		41	Peru	28.4
9	Nigeria	134.4		42	Nepal	27.7
10	Japan	128.2		43	Venezuela	27.2
11	Mexico	108.3		44	Uzbekistan	27.0
12	Vietnam	85.3		45	Malaysia	25.8
13	Philippines	84.5		46	Saudi Arabia	25.2
14	Germany	82.7		47	Taiwan	22.8
15	Ethiopia	79.3		48	Ghana	22.6
16	Egypt	75.4			North Korea	22.6
17	Turkey	74.2		50	Romania	21.6
18	Iran	70.3			Yemen	21.6
19	Thailand	64.8		52	Sri Lanka	20.9
20	France	60.7		53	Australia	20.4
21	United Kingdom	59.8		54	Mozambique	20.2
22	Congo-Kinshasa	59.3		55	Syria	19.5
23	Italy	58.1		56	Madagascar	19.1
24	Myanmar	51.0		57	Côte d'Ivoire	18.5
25	South Korea	48.0		58	Cameroon	16.6
26	South Africa	47.6		59	Chile	16.5
27	Colombia	46.3		60	Angola	16.4
28	Ukraine	46.0			Netherlands	16.4
29	Spain	43.4		62	Kazakhstan	14.8
30	Argentina	39.1		63	Cambodia	14.4
31	Tanzania	39.0			Niger	14.4
32	Poland	38.5		65	Mali	13.9
33	Sudan	37.0		66	Burkina Faso	13.6

Largest populations
Millions, 2050

1	India	1,592.7		15	Vietnam	116.7
2	China	1,392.3		16	Japan	112.2
3	United States	395.0		17	Russia	111.8
4	Pakistan	304.7		18	Iran	101.9
5	Indonesia	284.6		19	Turkey	101.2
6	Nigeria	258.1		20	Afghanistan	97.3
7	Brazil	253.1		21	Kenya	83.1
8	Bangladesh	242.9		22	Germany	78.8
9	Congo-Kinshasa	177.3		23	Thailand	74.6
10	Ethiopia	170.2		24	United Kingdom	67.1
11	Mexico	139.0		25	Tanzania	66.8
12	Philippines	127.1		26	Sudan	66.7
13	Uganda	126.9		27	Colombia	65.7
14	Egypt	125.9				

Fastest growing populations
Average annual % change, 2010–15

1	Niger	3.44	25	Equatorial Guinea	2.43
2	Timor-Leste	3.36	26	Guatemala	2.42
3	Burundi	3.22	27	Ethiopia	2.40
4	Uganda	3.21	28	Tanzania	2.36
5	Afghanistan	3.18	29	Gambia	2.32
6	Congo-Kinshasa	3.10	30	Sierra Leone	2.27
7	Liberia	3.09	31	Senegal	2.23
8	Guinea-Bissau	3.06	32	Mauritania	2.22
9	Mali	2.95	33	United Arab Emirates	2.13
10	Eritrea	2.94	34	Congo-Brazzaville	2.12
11	Yemen	2.90	35	Nigeria	2.09
12	West Bank and Gaza	2.87	36	Cape Verde	2.06
13	Angola	2.76	37	Saudi Arabia	2.05
	Benin	2.76	38	Kuwait	2.04
	Burkina Faso	2.76	39	Sudan	2.02
16	Somalia	2.74	40	Oman	1.95
17	Chad	2.73	41	Pakistan	1.90
18	Rwanda	2.72	42	Honduras	1.89
19	Guinea	2.65	43	Nepal	1.88
20	Iraq	2.60	44	Syria	1.85
21	Kenya	2.55	45	Côte d'Ivoire	1.84
22	Madagascar	2.48		Ghana	1.84
	Malawi	2.48		Zambia	1.84
24	Togo	2.44	48	Belize	1.83

Slowest growing populations
Average annual % change, 2010–15

1	Bulgaria	-0.80	23	Cuba	-0.01
2	Ukraine	-0.79		Italy	-0.01
3	Belarus	-0.57	25	Serbia	0.09
4	Russia	-0.56	26	Greece	0.10
5	Georgia	-0.53	27	Channel Islands	0.11
6	Romania	-0.53	28	Andorra	0.13
7	Latvia	-0.49	29	Denmark	0.14
8	Lithuania	-0.44		Martinique	0.14
9	Croatia	-0.34	31	Bermuda	0.15
	Moldova	-0.34		Montenegro	0.15
11	Estonia	-0.33		Netherlands	0.15
12	Hungary	-0.32		Portugal	0.15
13	Bosnia	-0.22	35	Taiwan	0.16
14	Japan	-0.18	36	Austria	0.17
15	Poland	-0.17		Belgium	0.17
16	Virgin Islands (US)	-0.15	38	South Korea	0.18
17	Germany	-0.13	39	Finland	0.23
18	Czech Republic	-0.09	40	Barbados	0.25
19	Slovenia	-0.08	41	North Korea	0.33
20	Armenia	-0.07	42	Uruguay	0.34
21	Macedonia	-0.04	43	Switzerland	0.35
22	Slovakia	-0.02	44	Trinidad & Tobago	0.37

Population: matters of breeding

Fertility rates, 2010–15

Highest av. no. of children per woman		Lowest av. no. of children per woman	
1 Niger	6.88	1 Macau	0.96
2 Guinea-Bissau	6.75	2 Hong Kong	0.99
3 Afghanistan	6.67	3 South Korea	1.21
4 Burundi	6.63	4 Belarus	1.23
5 Congo-Kinshasa	6.49	5 Ukraine	1.24
Liberia	6.49	6 Poland	1.25
7 Sierra Leone	6.16	7 Bosnia	1.26
8 Mali	6.06	8 Japan	1.27
9 Angola	6.04	9 Slovakia	1.28
10 Timor-Leste	6.00	10 Singapore	1.29
Uganda	6.00	11 Czech Republic	1.30
12 Chad	5.78	12 Lithuania	1.31
13 Somalia	5.61	13 Hungary	1.32
14 Burkina Faso	5.57	Romania	1.32
15 Rwanda	5.39	15 Latvia	1.33
16 Malawi	5.12	Slovenia	1.33
17 Equatorial Guinea	5.08	17 Bulgaria	1.34
18 Guinea	4.95	18 Russia	1.36
19 Yemen	4.93	19 Greece	1.38
20 Benin	4.92	Macedonia	1.38

Women[a] who use modern methods of contraception[b]

Highest, %		Lowest, %	
1 China	86	1 Somalia	1
2 Hong Kong	80	2 Chad	2
3 United Kingdom	79	3 Congo-Kinshasa	4
4 Finland	78	Guinea-Bissau	4
5 Netherlands	76	Sierra Leone	4
6 Australia	75	6 Angola	5
Belgium	75	Eritrea	5
8 Canada	73	Mauritania	5
Singapore	73	Niger	5
10 Costa Rica	72	10 Benin	6
Cuba	72	Guinea	6
Germany	72	Mali	6
New Zealand	72	13 Central African Rep	7
14 Brazil	70	Côte d'Ivoire	7
Thailand	70	Sudan	7
16 France	69	16 Albania	8
17 Colombia	68	Nigeria	8
Hungary	68	18 Afghanistan	9
Puerto Rico	68	Burkina Faso	9
United States	68	Gambia, The	9
21 South Korea	67	Papua New Guinea	9
22 Nicaragua	66	Timor-Leste	9
Vietnam	66	Togo	9
24 Austria	65		

a Married women aged 15–49. 2005 or latest available.
b Excludes traditional methods of contraception, such as the rhythm method.

Crude birth rates
Births per 1,000 population, 2007

Highest			Lowest		
1	Congo-Kinshasa	50	1	Germany	8
	Guinea-Bissau	50		Macau	8
	Liberia	50	3	Austria	9
4	Angola	49		Belarus	9
5	Mali	48		Bosnia	9
	Niger	48		Japan	9
	Sierra Leone	48		Lithuania	9
	Uganda	48		Slovenia	9
9	Afghanistan	47		South Korea	9
	Chad	47		Taiwan	9

Births per 1,000 women aged 15–19, 2005

1	Niger	244	14	Angola	138
2	Congo-Kinshasa	222	15	Nigeria	126
3	Liberia	219	16	Zambia	122
4	Uganda	203	17	Benin	120
5	Chad	189	18	Central African Rep	115
	Mali	189		Madagascar	115
7	Guinea-Bissau	188	20	Afghanistan	113
8	Guinea	176		Nicaragua	113
9	Timor-Leste	168	22	Gambia, The	109
10	Sierra Leone	160	23	Bangladesh	108
11	Burkina Faso	151	24	Côte d'Ivoire	107
12	Malawi	150		Guatemala	107
13	Congo-Brazzaville	143			

Sex ratio, males per 100 females, 2007

Highest			Lowest		
1	United Arab Emirates	210	1	Estonia	85
2	Qatar	203		Latvia	85
3	Kuwait	150	3	Russia	86
4	Bahrain	134		Ukraine	86
5	Oman	126	5	Armenia	87
6	Saudi Arabia	122		Belarus	87
7	Greenland	113		Lithuania	87
8	Bhutan	112		Netherlands Antilles	87
9	Afghanistan	107	9	Georgia	89
	Andorra	107		Lesotho	89
	Brunei	107	11	Martinique	90
	China	107		Virgin Islands (US)	90
	India	107	13	Hungary	91
	Libya	107	14	Aruba	92
15	Faroe Islands	106		Guadeloupe	92
	Jordan	106		Hong Kong	92
	Pakistan	106		Kazakhstan	92
18	Bangladesh	105		Macau	92
	French Polynesia	105		Moldova	92
20	Guam	104		Puerto Rico	92
	West Bank and Gaza	104			

Population: age

Median age[a]

Highest, 2007		
1	Japan	42.9
2	Italy	42.3
3	Germany	42.1
4	Andorra	42.0
5	Finland	40.9
6	Switzerland	40.8
7	Austria	40.6
	Belgium	40.6
	Bulgaria	40.6
	Croatia	40.6
11	Slovenia	40.2
12	Sweden	40.1
13	Channel Islands	39.7
	Greece	39.7
15	Denmark	39.5
	Latvia	39.5
	Portugal	39.5
18	France	39.3
	Netherlands	39.3
20	Bermuda	39.0
	Czech Republic	39.0
	Ukraine	39.0
	United Kingdom	39.0
24	Estonia	38.9
	Hong Kong	38.9
26	Hungary	38.8
27	Canada	38.6
	Spain	38.6
29	Norway	38.2
30	Luxembourg	38.1
	Malta	38.1
32	Bosnia	38.0
33	Belarus	37.8
	Lithuania	37.8
35	Singapore	37.5
36	Russia	37.3
37	Aruba	37.0
38	Romania	36.7
39	Australia	36.6
	Macau	36.6
41	Poland	36.5
	Serbia	36.5
43	Martinique	36.4
44	Netherlands Antilles	36.2
45	United States	36.1
46	New Zealand	35.8
47	Cuba	35.6
	Slovakia	35.6

Lowest, 2007		
1	Uganda	14.8
2	Niger	15.5
3	Mali	15.8
4	Burkina Faso	16.2
	Guinea-Bissau	16.2
6	Chad	16.3
	Congo-Brazzaville	16.3
	Congo-Kinshasa	16.3
	Liberia	16.3
	Malawi	16.3
11	Yemen	16.5
12	Afghanistan	16.7
	Angola	16.7
	Zambia	16.7
15	Burundi	17.0
16	West Bank and Gaza	17.1
17	Eritrea	17.4
18	Ethiopia	17.5
	Nigeria	17.5
	Rwanda	17.5
21	Benin	17.6
	Equatorial Guinea	17.6
23	Mozambique	17.7
24	Madagascar	17.8
25	Kenya	17.9
	Somalia	17.9
	Togo	17.9
28	Guinea	18.0
29	Central African Rep	18.1
	Guatemala	18.1
	Swaziland	18.1
32	Senegal	18.2
	Tanzania	18.2
34	Mauritania	18.4
	Sierra Leone	18.4
	Timor-Leste	18.4
37	Côte d'Ivoire	18.5
38	Namibia	18.6
39	Zimbabwe	18.7
40	Cameroon	18.8
41	Iraq	19.1
	Laos	19.1
43	Lesotho	19.2
44	Cape Verde	19.3
	Tajikistan	19.3
46	Gabon	19.4
47	Nicaragua	19.7
	Papua New Guinea	19.7

a Age at which there are an equal number of people above and below.

Ageing index

Number of people aged 60 or over for every 100 people under 15, 2007

Highest		Lowest	
1 Japan	201.0	1 Niger	6.6
2 Italy	189.8	2 Uganda	7.4
3 Germany	182.3	3 Liberia	7.7
4 Bulgaria	172.5	4 United Arab Emirates	7.9
5 Greece	166.0	5 Yemen	8.0
6 Latvia	164.4	6 Angola	8.5
7 Austria	156.1	7 Mali	8.6
8 Slovenia	155.9	8 Burkina Faso	8.9
9 Czech Republic	150.7	Congo-Kinshasa	8.9
10 Croatia	150.0	10 Eritrea	9.0
11 Ukraine	149.5	11 Burundi	9.2
12 Spain	149.2	12 Rwanda	9.3
13 Estonia	148.3	13 Congo-Brazzaville	9.4
14 Portugal	144.3	Somalia	9.4
15 Switzerland	142.9	15 Afghanistan	9.5
16 Sweden	142.8	16 Kenya	9.6
17 Hungary	140.1	17 Chad	9.7
18 Belgium	139.2	Guinea-Bissau	9.7
19 Finland	134.3	19 West Bank and Gaza	9.8
Lithuania	134.3	20 Malawi	9.9
21 Romania	130.3	21 Benin	10.0
22 Belarus	126.9	22 Papua New Guinea	10.2
23 Channel Islands	126.3	23 Zambia	10.3
24 Bosnia	125.5	24 Ethiopia	10.7
25 United Kingdom	124.7	25 Nigeria	11.0
26 France	121.1	26 Madagascar	11.1
27 Malta	119.9	27 Iraq	11.2
28 Denmark	117.9	28 Togo	11.4
29 Hong Kong	116.1	29 Senegal	11.8
30 Russia	114.0	Timor-Leste	11.8
31 Netherlands	112.6	31 Mozambique	12.0
32 Poland	112.3	32 Mauritania	12.3
33 Canada	110.3	33 Tanzania	12.4
34 Norway	108.0	34 Qatar	12.6
35 Slovakia	106.1	35 Sierra Leone	12.8
36 Serbia	105.4	36 Saudi Arabia	12.9
37 Georgia	101.2	37 Côte d'Ivoire	13.0
38 Luxembourg	98.6	Oman	13.0
39 Australia	95.0	39 Equatorial Guinea	13.2
40 Cyprus	91.8	Guinea	13.2
41 Cuba	87.4	41 Laos	13.3
42 Macedonia	85.5	Nicaragua	13.3
43 Martinique	84.3	Syria	13.3
44 New Zealand	84.0	44 Tajikistan	13.4
45 United States	83.9	45 Cape Verde	13.5
46 South Korea	83.4	46 Namibia	13.8
47 Moldova	81.6	47 Cameroon	14.0
48 Puerto Rico	81.1	48 Kuwait	14.1
49 Macau	79.7	49 Central African Republic	14.2
50 Virgin Islands (US)	79.5	Zimbabwe	14.2

City living

Biggest cities[a]
Population m, 2005

1	Tokyo, Japan	35.3		Jakarta, Indonesia	8.8
2	Mexico City, Mexico	18.7		Lagos, Nigeria	8.8
	New York, US	18.7	25	London, UK	8.5
4	São Paulo, Brazil	18.3	26	Guangzhou, China	8.4
5	Mumbai, India	18.2	27	Lima, Peru	7.7
6	Delhi, India	15.1		Tehran, Iran	7.7
7	Shanghai, China	14.5	29	Bogotá, Colombia	7.4
8	Kolkata, India	14.3	30	Shenzhen, China	7.2
9	Buenos Aires, Argentina	12.6	31	Hong Kong	7.1
	Dhaka, Bangladesh	12.6		Kinshasa, Congo	7.1
11	Los Angeles, US	12.3		Tianjin, China	7.1
12	Karachi, Pakistan	11.6		Wuhan, China	7.1
13	Cairo, Egypt	11.5	35	Chennai, India	6.9
	Rio de Janeiro, Brazil	11.5	36	Bangkok, Thailand	6.6
15	Osaka, Japan	11.3	37	Bangalore, India	6.5
16	Manila, Philippines	10.8	38	Chongqing, China	6.4
17	Beijing, China	10.7	39	Lahore, Pakistan	6.3
18	Moscow, Russia	10.4	40	Hyderabad, India	6.1
19	Paris, France	9.9	41	Santiago, Chile	5.6
20	Seoul, South Korea	9.8	42	Madrid, Spain	5.4
21	Istanbul, Turkey	9.7		Miami, US	5.4
22	Chicago, US	8.8		Philadelphia, US	5.4

Proportion of a country's population residing in a single city[b]
%, 2005

1	Hong Kong	100.0	20	Lima, Peru	28.4
2	Singapore	100.0	21	San José, Costa Rica	28.1
3	Kuwait City, Kuwait	69.9	22	Tokyo, Japan	27.6
4	San Juan, Puerto Rico	66.0	23	Vienna, Austria	27.3
5	Montevideo, Uruguay	45.9	24	Lisbon, Portugal	26.2
6	Tel Aviv, Israel	45.0	25	Dublin, Ireland	25.0
7	Beirut, Lebanon	44.3	26	Tbilisi, Georgia	24.4
8	Panama City, Panama	37.6	27	Baku, Azerbaijan	22.4
9	Yerevan, Armenia	36.5	28	Luanda, Angola	22.0
10	Tripoli, Libya	35.4	29	Santo Domingo, Dom. Rep.	21.8
11	Santiago, Chile	34.4	30	Lomé, Togo	21.1
12	Brazzaville, Congo-Brazz.	33.7	31	Sydney, Australia	21.0
13	Ulan Bator, Mongolia	33.2	32	Helsinki, Finland	20.9
14	Monrovia, Liberia	33.1	33	Dakar, Senegal	20.7
15	Buenos Aires, Argentina	32.4	34	San Salvador, El Salvador	20.6
16	Dubai, United Arab Em.	31.0	35	Seoul, South Korea	20.5
17	Asunción, Paraguay	29.8	36	Port-au-Prince, Haiti	20.3
18	Athens, Greece	29.1	37	Copenhagen, Denmark	20.0
19	Auckland, New Zealand	29.0	38	Havana, Cuba	19.4

a Urban agglomerations. Data may change from year-to-year based on reassessments of agglomeration boundaries.
b Urban agglomerations over 750,000.

Refugees and asylum seekers[a]

Largest refugee nationalities
'000, 2006

1	Afghanistan	2,107.5	11	Myanmar	202.8
2	Iraq	1,450.9	12	Bosnia	200.0
3	Sudan	868.3	13	Eritrea	193.7
4	Somalia	464.0	14	Serbia	174.0
5	Congo-Kinshasa	401.9	15	Liberia	160.6
6	Burundi	396.5	16	Russia	159.4
7	Vietnam	374.3	17	China	140.6
8	West Bank and Gaza	334.1	18	Azerbaijan	126.1
9	Turkey	227.2	19	Sri Lanka	117.0
10	Angola	206.5	20	Bhutan	108.1

Countries with largest refugee populations
'000, 2006

1	Pakistan	1,044.5	11	Kenya	272.5
2	Iran	968.4	12	Uganda	272.0
3	United States	843.5	13	Saudi Arabia	240.8
4	Syria	702.2	14	Congo-Kinshasa	208.4
5	Germany	605.4	15	Sudan	196.2
6	Jordan	500.2	16	India	158.4
7	Tanzania	485.3	17	Canada	151.8
8	United Kingdom	301.6	18	France	145.0
9	China	301.0	19	Thailand	133.1
10	Chad	286.7	20	Nepal	128.2

Origin of asylum applications to indust. countries
'000, 2006

1	Iraq	22.2	11	Mexico	6.8
2	China	18.3	12	Bangladesh	6.4
3	Russia	15.7	13	Eritrea	6.3
	Serbia	15.7		Nigeria	6.3
5	Turkey	8.7	15	Colombia	6.1
6	Afghanistan	8.4	16	Sri Lanka	5.7
7	Iran	8.3	17	Congo-Kinshasa	5.5
8	Pakistan	7.6	18	India	5.4
9	Somalia	7.3	19	Armenia	4.2
10	Haiti	7.0	20	Syria	3.7

Asylum applications in industrialised countries
'000, 2006

1	United States	51.5	10	Belgium	11.6
2	France	30.7	11	Switzerland	10.6
3	United Kingdom	27.9	12	Italy	10.1
4	Sweden	24.3	13	Norway	5.3
5	Canada	22.9		Spain	5.3
6	Germany	21.0	15	Cyprus	4.6
7	Netherlands	14.5		Turkey	4.6
8	Austria	13.4	17	Ireland	4.3
9	Greece	12.3	18	Poland	4.2

a As reported by UNHCR.

The world economy

Biggest economies
GDP, $bn, 2006

1	United States	13,164		24	Poland	339
2	Japan	4,368		25	Norway	335
3	Germany	2,897		26	Austria	322
4	China	2,645		27	Greece	308
5	United Kingdom	2,377		28	Denmark	275
6	France[a]	2,248		29	South Africa	255
7	Italy	1,851		30	Ireland	220
8	Canada	1,272		31	Iran	218
9	Spain	1,225		32	Argentina	214
10	Brazil	1,067		33	Finland	211
11	Russia	987		34	Thailand	206
12	India	912		35	Portugal	195
13	South Korea	888		36	Hong Kong	190
14	Mexico	839		37	Venezuela	182
15	Australia	781		38	Colombia	153
16	Netherlands	662		39	Malaysia	151
17	Turkey	403		40	Chile	146
18	Belgium	394		41	Czech Republic	143
19	Sweden	384		42	Israel	140
20	Switzerland	380		43	Singapore	132
21	Indonesia	365		44	United Arab Emirates[b]	130
	Taiwan	365		45	Pakistan	127
23	Saudi Arabia	349		46	Romania	122

Biggest economies by purchasing power
GDP PPP, $bn, 2006

1	United States	13,164		23	Thailand	482
2	China	6,092		24	Argentina	469
3	Japan	4,081		25	South Africa	431
4	India	2,740		26	Pakistan	375
5	Germany	2,663		27	Egypt	367
6	United Kingdom	2,003		28	Belgium	354
7	France	1,960		29	Greece	350
8	Russia	1,869		30	Malaysia	327
9	Italy	1,710		31	Sweden	311
10	Brazil	1,694		32	Austria	299
11	Mexico	1,269			Venezuela	299
12	Spain	1,264		34	Colombia	291
13	Canada	1,199			Ukraine	291
14	South Korea	1,113		36	Switzerland	279
15	Indonesia	770		37	Philippines	272
16	Australia	736		38	Hong Kong	268
17	Taiwan	722		39	Nigeria	233
18	Iran	694			Norway	233
19	Turkey	614		41	Czech Republic	227
20	Netherlands	597		42	Romania	225
21	Poland	566		43	Portugal	220
22	Saudi Arabia	528		44	Chile	214

a Includes overseas departments. b 2005

Regional GDP

$bn, 2007		*% annual growth 2002–07*	
World	54,312	World	4.6
Advanced economies	39,131	Advanced economies	2.7
G7	30,419	G7	2.4
Euro area (15)	12,158	Euro area (15)	2.0
Asia[a]	5,724	Asia[a]	9.0
Latin America	3,450	Latin America	4.8
Eastern Europe[b]	3,527	Eastern Europe[b]	6.9
Middle East	1,387	Middle East	6.0
Africa	1,092	Africa	5.9

Regional purchasing power

GDP, % of total, 2007		*$ per head, 2007*	
World	100.0	World	9,730
Advanced economies	56.4	Advanced economies	35,780
G7	43.5	G7	37,380
Euro area (15)	16.1	Euro area (15)	32,940
Asia[a]	20.1	Asia[a]	3,840
Latin America	8.3	Latin America	9,760
Eastern Europe[b]	8.6	Eastern Europe[b]	11,700
Middle East	3.8	Middle East	10,350
Africa	3.0	Africa	2,420

Regional population

% of total (6.7bn), 2007		*No. of countries[c], 2007*	
Advanced economies	15.3	Advanced economies	31
G7	11.3	G7	7
Euro area (15)	4.7	Euro area (15)	15
Asia[a]	52.6	Asia[a]	23
Latin America	8.6	Latin America	32
Eastern Europe[b]	7.1	Eastern Europe[b]	26
Middle East	3.7	Middle East	13
Africa	12.8	Africa	47

Regional international trade

Exports of goods & services, % of tot., 2007		*Current account balances, $bn, 2007*	
Advanced economies	66.4	Advanced economies	-463
G7	38.4	G7	-544
Euro area (15)	29.5	Euro area (15)	-30
Asia[a]	13.2	Asia[a]	384
Latin America	5.1	Latin America	16
Eastern Europe[b]	8.0	Eastern Europe[b]	-45
Middle East	4.7	Middle East	275
Africa	2.5	Africa	2

a Excludes Hong Kong, Japan, Singapore, South Korea and Taiwan.
b Includes Russia, other CIS and Turkey.
c IMF definition.

Living standards

Highest GDP per head
$, 2006

1	Luxembourg	87,490	36	Guadeloupe[b]	23,880
2	Norway	72,810	37	Cyprus	23,430
3	Bermuda[ac]	68,180	38	Aruba[ab]	22,810
4	Qatar	59,570		Martinique[b]	22,810
5	Iceland	54,400	40	Bahrain[b]	22,620
6	Ireland	52,410	41	Israel	20,660
7	Switzerland	52,110	42	Bahamas[a]	20,130
8	Denmark	50,990	43	Puerto Rico[a]	18,720
9	United States	43,730	44	Slovenia	18,650
10	Channel Islands[ab]	49,680	45	Portugal	18,550
11	Cayman Islands[ac]	43,090	46	South Korea	18,500
12	Sweden	42,180	47	Réunion[b]	18,230
13	Netherlands	40,380	48	Taiwan	15,990
14	Finland	39,750	49	Malta	15,940
	United Kingdom	39,750	50	Equatorial Guinea	15,860
16	Austria	39,270	51	New Caledonia[ad]	15,070
17	Andorra[ab]	39,010	52	Guam[ab]	14,620
	Canada	39,010	53	Virgin Islands (US)[ac]	14,470
19	Australia	38,260	54	Czech Republic	14,020
20	Belgium	37,890	55	Trinidad & Tobago	13,950
21	France	37,040	56	Saudi Arabia	13,850
22	Kuwait	36,460	57	French Polynesia[ae]	13,620
23	Faroe Islands[ab]	36,170	58	Estonia	12,620
24	Germany	35,030	59	Netherlands Antilles[ac]	12,610
25	Japan	34,080	60	Barbados	12,340
26	Italy	31,860	61	Oman[b]	11,860
27	Brunei	31,420	62	Hungary	11,180
28	Macau	31,340	63	Slovakia	10,190
29	Greenland[ab]	30,360	64	Croatia	9,330
30	Singapore	30,040	65	Chile	8,840
31	Spain	28,220	66	Poland	8,800
32	Greece	27,790	67	Latvia	8,750
33	United Arab Emirates[b]	27,600		Lithuania	8,750
34	Hong Kong	26,730	69	Libya	8,390
35	New Zealand	25,490	70	Mexico	7,750

Lowest GDP per head
$, 2006

1	Burundi	120	11	Zimbabwe[b]	260
2	Congo-Kinshasa	140	12	Afghanistan	270
3	Ethiopia	170		Rwanda	270
4	Guinea-Bissau	190	14	Madagascar	290
	Liberia	190		Somalia[a]	290
6	Myanmar	230	16	Gambia, The	320
7	Eritrea	240		Nepal	320
	Malawi	240		Uganda	320
9	Niger	250	19	Tanzania	330
	Sierra Leone	250	20	Mozambique	340

a Estimate.   b 2005   c 2004   d 2003   e 2002

Highest purchasing power

GDP per head in PPP (USA = 100), 2006

1	Luxembourg	172.0	36	Spain	65.2
2	Qatar[b]	160.8	37	Equatorial Guinea	61.8
3	Bermuda[ac]	159.0	38	Cyprus	58.9
4	Channel Islands[b]	117.9	39	New Zealand	58.0
5	Norway	113.9	40	Slovenia	55.4
6	Brunei	113.5	41	Israel	54.8
7	Singapore	101.7	42	Bahamas[b]	52.5
8	Macau	100.0	43	South Korea	52.3
	United States	100.0	44	Saudi Arabia	50.7
10	Cayman Islands[ac]	99.6	45	Czech Republic	50.3
11	Kuwait[b]	99.1	46	Aruba[ac]	49.6
12	Ireland	91.6	47	Malta	49.4
13	Hong Kong	88.8	48	Martinique[b]	47.9
14	Andorra[ab]	88.2	49	Portugal	47.3
15	Switzerland	84.6	50	Oman[b]	46.3
16	Iceland	84.0	51	Greenland[ae]	45.5
17	Canada	83.5	52	Guadeloupe[b]	44.7
18	Netherlands	83.2	53	Puerto Rico[a]	43.4
19	Austria	82.0	54	Estonia	43.1
20	Denmark	81.2	55	Hungary	41.6
21	Australia	80.8	56	Slovak Republic	40.3
22	Isle of Man[ab]	79.6		Trinidad & Tobago	40.3
23	Sweden	77.8	58	French Polynesia[ad]	39.8
24	Belgium	76.3	59	Réunion[b]	39.0
25	United Arab Emirates[b]	76.2	60	Netherlands Antilles[ac]	36.4
26	Bahrain[b]	76.1	61	Barbados[b]	36.2
27	United Kingdom	75.3	62	Lithuania	35.8
28	Finland	75.1	63	Latvia	34.9
29	Germany	73.5	64	Guam[ab]	34.1
30	France	72.8		New Caledonia[ad]	34.1
31	Japan	72.7	66	Poland	33.7
32	Taiwan[a]	72.3	67	Virgin Islands (US)[ac]	33.0
33	Greece	71.4	68	Croatia	32.5
34	Faroe Islands[ae]	70.5	69	Gabon	32.3
35	Italy	66.1	70	Russia	29.8

Lowest purchasing power

GDP per head in PPP (USA = 100), 2006

1	Congo-Kinshasa	0.6		Central African Rep	1.6
2	Burundi	0.8		Malawi	1.6
	Liberia	0.8	12	Rwanda	1.7
4	Guinea-Bissau	1.1		Mozambique	1.7
5	Somalia[a]	1.4	14	Togo	1.8
	Niger	1.4	15	Myanmar[b]	1.9
	Sierra Leone	1.4	16	Madagascar	2.0
	Ethiopia	1.4		Uganda	2.0
9	Eritrea	1.6			

a Estimate. b 2005 c 2004 d 2003 e 2001

The quality of life

Human development index[a]

Highest, 2005

1	Iceland	96.8	31	Barbados	89.2
	Norway	96.8	32	Czech Republic	89.1
3	Australia	96.2		Kuwait	89.1
4	Canada	96.1	34	Malta	87.8
5	Ireland	95.9	35	Qatar	87.5
6	Sweden	95.6	36	Hungary	87.4
7	Switzerland	95.5	37	Poland	87.0
8	Japan	95.3	38	Argentina	86.9
	Netherlands	95.3	39	United Arab Emirates	86.8
10	Finland	95.2	40	Chile	86.7
	France	95.2	41	Bahrain	86.6
12	United States	95.1	42	Slovakia	86.3
13	Denmark	94.9	43	Lithuania	86.2
	Spain	94.9	44	Estonia	86.0
15	Austria	94.8	45	Latvia	85.5
16	Belgium	94.6	46	Uruguay	85.2
	United Kingdom	94.6	47	Croatia	85.0
18	Luxembourg	94.4	48	Costa Rica	84.6
19	New Zealand	94.3	49	Bahamas	84.5
20	Italy	94.1	50	Cuba	83.8
21	Hong Kong	93.7	51	Mexico	82.9
22	Germany	93.5	52	Bulgaria	82.4
23	Israel	93.2	53	Libya	81.8
24	Greece	92.6	54	Oman	81.4
25	Singapore	92.2		Trinidad & Tobago	81.4
26	South Korea	92.1	56	Romania	81.3
27	Slovenia	91.7	57	Panama	81.2
28	Cyprus	90.3		Saudi Arabia	81.2
29	Portugal	89.7	59	Malaysia	81.1
30	Brunei	89.4			

Human development index[a]

Lowest, 2005

1	Sierra Leone	33.6	10	Congo-Kinshasa	41.1
2	Burkina Faso	37.0	11	Burundi	41.3
3	Guinea-Bissau	37.4	12	Côte d'Ivoire	43.2
	Niger	37.4	13	Zambia	43.4
5	Mali	38.0	14	Benin	43.7
6	Central African Rep	38.4		Malawi	43.7
	Mozambique	38.4	16	Angola	44.6
8	Chad	38.8	17	Rwanda	45.2
9	Ethiopia	40.6	18	Guinea	45.6

a GDP or GDP per head is often taken as a measure of how developed a country is, but its usefulness is limited as it refers only to economic welfare. In 1990 the UN Development Programme published its first estimate of a Human Development Index, which combined statistics on two other indicators – adult literacy and life expectancy – with income levels to give a better, though still far from perfect, indicator of human development. In 1991 average years of schooling was combined with adult literacy to give a knowledge variable. The HDI is shown here scaled from 0 to 100; countries scoring over 80 are considered to have high human development, those scoring from 50 to 79 medium and those under 50 low.

Economic freedom index[a], 2008

1	Hong Kong	90.3		21	Barbados	71.3
2	Singapore	87.4			Cyprus	71.3
3	Ireland	82.4		23	Germany	71.2
4	Australia	82.0		24	Bahamas	71.1
5	United States	80.6		25	Taiwan	71.0
6	Canada	80.2		26	Lithuania	70.8
	New Zealand	80.2		27	Sweden	70.4
8	Chile	79.8		28	Armenia	70.3
9	Switzerland	79.7		29	Trinidad & Tobago	70.2
10	United Kingdom	79.5		30	Austria	70.0
11	Denmark	79.2		31	Spain	69.7
12	Estonia	77.8		32	El Salvador	69.2
13	Netherlands	76.8			Georgia	69.2
14	Iceland	76.5		34	Norway	69.0
15	Luxembourg	75.2		35	Slovakia	68.7
16	Finland	74.8		36	Botswana	68.6
17	Japan	72.5		37	Czech Republic	68.5
18	Mauritius	72.3		38	Kuwait	68.3
19	Bahrain	72.2			Latvia	68.3
20	Belgium	71.5		40	Uruguay	68.1

Privacy[b]

Highest, 2007 (1=highest surveillance; 5=lowest surveillance)

1	China	1.3			Sweden	2.1
	Malaysia	1.3		20	Australia	2.2
	Russia	1.3			Israel	2.2
4	Singapore	1.4			Japan	2.2
	United Kingdom	1.4			Latvia	2.2
6	Taiwan	1.5		24	Austria	2.3
	Thailand	1.5			Cyprus	2.3
	United States	1.5			New Zealand	2.3
9	Philippines	1.8			Poland	2.3
10	France	1.9			South Africa	2.3
	India	1.9			Spain	2.3
12	Bulgaria	2.0		30	Malta	2.4
	Denmark	2.0			Switzerland	2.4
	Lithuania	2.0		32	Czech Republic	2.5
15	Brazil	2.1			Finland	2.5
	Netherlands	2.1			Ireland	2.5
	Norway	2.1		35	Belgium	2.7
	Slovakia	2.1			Iceland	2.7

a Ranks countries on the basis of indicators of how government intervention can restrict the economic relations between individuals, published by the Heritage Foundation. The ranking includes data on labour and business freedom as well as trade policy, taxation, monetary policy, the banking system, foreign-investment rules, property rights, the amount of economic output consumed by the government, regulation policy, the size of the black market and the extent of wage and price controls. Countries are scored from 80–100 (free) to 0–49.9 (repressed).

b Ranks EU countries and a benchmark group of non-EU countres. Levels of surveillance are ranked by combining criteria such as: level of legal protection; privacy enforcement; use of identity cards and biometrics; data-sharing; visual surveillance; communication interception; workplace monitoring.

Economic growth

Highest economic growth, 1996–2006
Average annual % increase in real GDP

1	Equatorial Guinea	33.7		28	Bahrain	7.2
2	Liberia	15.0			Lithuania	7.2
3	Azerbaijan	13.4		30	Georgia	7.1
4	Turkmenistan	13.3			Laos	7.1
5	Myanmar	12.6		32	Belize	6.8
6	Qatar[a]	11.7		33	Burkina Faso	6.6
7	Armenia	10.5			Dominican Republic	6.6
8	China	10.3		35	Tanzania	6.4
9	Cambodia	9.9		36	Kuwait[a]	6.3
10	Trinidad & Tobago	9.6			Uganda	6.3
11	Mozambique	9.4		38	Bangladesh	6.2
12	Chad	9.3		39	Luxembourg	6.0
13	Angola	9.0		40	Costa Rica	5.9
14	Estonia	8.7			Mongolia	5.9
15	Bhutan	8.6			Singapore	5.9
	Latvia	8.6		43	Albania	5.7
17	Kazakhstan	8.2			Gambia, The	5.7
18	Tajikistan	8.1			Jordan	5.7
19	Ireland	8.0		46	Egypt	5.6
	Nigeria	8.0			Mali	5.6
21	Belarus	7.9			Panama	5.6
	Vietnam	7.9		49	Ethiopia	5.5
23	Rwanda	7.7			Russia	5.5
24	Botswana	7.5			Uzbekistan	5.5
25	United Arab Emirates	7.4		52	Ghana	5.4
26	India	7.3			Sri Lanka	5.4
	Sudan	7.3			Tunisia	5.4

Lowest economic growth, 1996–2006
Average annual % change in real GDP

1	Congo-Kinshasa[a]	0.8		20	Austria	2.5
	Côte d'Ivoire	0.8			Portugal	2.5
	Gabon	0.8		22	Barbados	2.6
4	Eritrea	0.9			Belgium	2.6
	Haiti	0.9			France	2.6
	Papua New Guinea	0.9		25	Syria[a]	2.7
7	Jamaica	1.0		26	Brazil	2.8
8	Japan	1.2			Indonesia	2.8
9	Togo	1.4			Romania	2.8
10	Germany	1.6			Swaziland	2.8
11	Central African Rep	1.7		30	Argentina	2.9
	Italy	1.7			Colombia	2.9
	Paraguay	1.7			Netherlands	2.9
14	Uruguay	1.8		33	Lesotho	3.0
15	Burundi[a]	2.1			Norway	3.0
	Switzerland	2.1			Thailand	3.0
	West Bank and Gaza	2.1			Venezuela	3.0
18	Denmark	2.4		37	Lebanon[a]	3.1
	Fiji	2.4				

a Estimate.

Highest economic growth, 1986–96
Average annual % increase in real GDP

1	Equatorial Guinea	15.0	11	Botswana	8.5
2	China	11.4	12	Cambodia	8.1
3	Thailand	10.6	13	Vietnam	7.9
4	Singapore	10.3	14	Indonesia	7.7
5	Malaysia	10.1	15	Mauritius	7.4
6	Belize	10.0	16	Uganda	7.2
7	South Korea	9.3	17	Mozambique	6.9
8	Bhutan	8.8		Swaziland	6.9
	Chile	8.8		Syria	6.9
10	Taiwan	8.6	20	United Arab Emirates	6.7

Lowest economic growth, 1986–96
Average annual % change in real GDP

1	Liberia	-21.8	11	Albania	-0.9
2	Bulgaria	-5.3	12	Hungary	-0.8
3	Congo-Kinshasa	-4.7	13	Haiti	-0.7
	Sierra Leone	-4.7	14	Burundi	-0.6
5	Rwanda	-4.3	15	Zambia	-0.3
6	Lebanon	-2.8	16	Mongolia	-0.2
7	Cameroon	-2.5	17	Nicaragua	0.1
8	Romania	-2.0	18	Suriname	0.3
9	Central African Rep	-1.9	19	Czech Republic	0.5
10	Libya	-1.0			

Highest services growth, 1996–2006
Average annual % increase in real terms

1	Azerbaijan	13.7	10	Estonia	8.8
2	Armenia	11.2	11	Mauritania	8.7
	Bhutan	11.2	12	Rwanda	8.6
4	China	11.0	13	Belarus	8.4
5	Cambodia	10.2		Uganda	8.4
6	India	9.6	15	Ireland[a]	7.9
7	Georgia	9.2		Kazakhstan	7.9
8	Latvia	9.1	17	Albania	7.7
9	United Arab Emirates[a]	8.9	18	Dominican Republic	7.6

Lowest services growth, 1996–2006
Average annual % change in real terms

1	Zimbabwe[a]	-5.5	8	Italy	2.0
2	Guinea-Bissau	-1.1		Uruguay	2.0
3	Paraguay	1.4		Thailand	2.0
4	Japan[a]	1.7	11	Austria	2.3
5	Jamaica	1.8	12	Denmark	2.4
6	Germany	1.9	13	Belgium	2.6
	Switzerland[a]	1.9		Guinea	2.6

a 1995–2005

Trading places

Biggest exporters

% of total world exports (goods, services and income), 2006

1	Euro area (12)	16.60	23	India	1.19
2	United States	12.11	24	Malaysia	1.10
3	Germany	8.90	25	Norway	1.08
4	United Kingdom	6.50	26	Australia	1.04
5	China	6.43	27	Hong Kong	1.03
6	Japan	5.19	28	Denmark	0.99
7	France	4.54	29	Luxembourg	0.97
8	Netherlands	3.47	30	Brazil	0.95
9	Italy	3.40	31	Thailand	0.91
10	Canada	2.98	32	Poland	0.82
11	Belgium	2.37	33	United Arab Emirates	0.81
12	South Korea	2.30	34	Turkey	0.70
13	Spain	2.15	35	Czech Republic	0.66
14	Russia	2.11	36	Finland	0.65
15	Switzerland	1.90	37	Indonesia	0.59
16	Taiwan	1.62	38	Hungary	0.54
17	Mexico	1.58	39	South Africa	0.47
18	Ireland	1.44	40	Kuwait	0.46
19	Sweden	1.41	41	Iran	0.43
20	Singapore	1.34		Portugal	0.43
21	Saudi Arabia	1.32		Venezuela	0.43
22	Austria	1.20	44	Israel	0.41

Most trade dependent

Trade as % of GDPᵃ, 2006

1	Aruba	172.5
2	Singapore	95.8
3	Malaysia	94.6
4	United Arab Emirates	91.4
5	Slovakia	77.6
6	Swaziland	74.3
7	Belgium	70.9
8	Vietnam	68.9
9	Lesotho	68.7
10	Puerto Rico	68.6
11	Estonia	67.1
12	Hungary	66.3
	Netherlands Antilles	66.3
14	Czech Republic	65.5
15	Equatorial Guinea	64.8
16	Bahrain	63.2
17	Iraq	61.9
18	Tajikistan	61.7
19	Zimbabwe	61.4
20	Taiwan	59.5
21	Slovenia	59.3

Least trade dependent

Trade as % of GDPᵃ, 2006

1	North Korea	6.2
2	Brazil	10.7
3	United States	11.0
4	Central African Rep	12.1
5	Bermuda	12.4
6	Rwanda	12.7
7	Japan	13.2
8	Greece	13.8
9	Cuba	15.1
10	Burkina Faso	15.3
11	Hong Kong	15.5
12	India	15.9
13	Benin	16.2
14	Colombia	16.3
	Euro area (12)	16.3
16	Australia	16.6
17	Sudan	17.0
18	Burundi	17.1
19	Pakistan	17.2
20	Uganda	17.2
21	Cameroon	17.9

Notes: The figures are drawn wherever possible from balance of payment statistics so have differing definitions from trade statistics taken from customs or similar sources. For Hong Kong and Singapore, domestic exports and retained imports only are used.
a Average of imports plus exports of goods as % of GDP.

Biggest traders of goods
% of world exports of goods, 2006

1	Euro area (12)	15.13	25	Thailand	1.10
2	Germany	9.76	26	Australia	1.08
3	United States	8.86	27	India	1.07
4	China	8.37	28	Norway	1.06
5	Japan	5.31	29	Poland	1.01
6	France	4.15	30	Ireland	0.90
7	United Kingdom	3.88	31	Czech Republic	0.82
8	Italy	3.60	32	Turkey	0.79
9	Canada	3.47	33	Denmark	0.78
10	Netherlands	3.34	34	Indonesia	0.74
11	South Korea	2.86	35	Finland	0.67
12	Russia	2.62	36	Hungary	0.64
13	Belgium	2.43		Iran	0.64
14	Mexico	2.16	38	Venezuela	0.56
15	Taiwan	2.02	39	South Africa	0.55
16	Spain	1.87	40	Puerto Rico	0.52
17	Saudi Arabia	1.82	41	Kuwait	0.51
18	Switzerland	1.44	42	Chile	0.50
19	Malaysia	1.39	43	Algeria	0.47
20	Sweden	1.28	44	Nigeria	0.45
21	Singapore	1.23	45	Argentina	0.40
22	United Arab Emirates	1.20		Philippines	0.40
23	Brazil	1.19	47	Israel	0.38
24	Austria	1.16		Portugal	0.38

Biggest traders of services and income
% of world exports of services and income, 2006

1	Euro area (12)	19.56	24	Russia	1.06
2	United States	18.69	25	Australia	0.96
3	United Kingdom	11.80	26	Taiwan	0.82
4	Germany	7.15	27	Greece	0.70
5	France	5.32	28	Finland	0.60
6	Japan	4.95	29	Malaysia	0.53
7	Netherlands	3.73		Portugal	0.53
8	Italy	2.99	31	Turkey	0.51
9	Switzerland	2.84	32	Thailand	0.50
10	Spain	2.72	33	Israel	0.48
11	Hong Kong	2.71	34	Brazil	0.45
12	Luxembourg	2.64	35	Poland	0.43
13	Ireland	2.53	36	Mexico	0.40
14	China	2.50	37	Kuwait	0.38
15	Belgium	2.27	38	Czech Republic	0.33
16	Canada	1.99		Egypt	0.33
17	Sweden	1.67		Hungary	0.33
18	Singapore	1.56	41	Saudi Arabia	0.31
19	India	1.45		South Africa	0.31
20	Denmark	1.40	43	Indonesia	0.27
21	Austria	1.27	44	Lebanon	0.24
22	South Korea	1.14	45	Argentina	0.23
23	Norway	1.12	46	Ukraine	0.22

Balance of payments: current account

Largest surpluses
$m, 2006

1	China	249,866		26	Belgium	10,671
2	Japan	170,520		27	Austria	10,259
3	Germany	150,750		28	Indonesia	9,937
4	Saudi Arabia	99,066		29	Argentina	8,092
5	Russia	94,257		30	Israel	7,990
6	Norway	58,323		31	Denmark	7,339
7	Netherlands	55,795		32	South Korea	6,092
8	Switzerland	54,849		33	Philippines	5,897
9	Kuwait	50,996		34	Iraq[a]	5,666
10	Singapore	36,326		35	Chile	5,256
11	United Arab Emirates	35,942		36	Brunei	5,232
12	Algeria	28,950		37	Trinidad & Tobago	4,654
13	Sweden	28,413		38	Oman	4,377
14	Venezuela	27,149		39	Luxembourg	4,370
15	Malaysia	25,488		40	Azerbaijan	3,708
16	Taiwan	24,655		41	Turkmenistan	3,351
17	Libya	22,170		42	Uzbekistan	3,198
18	Canada	20,797		43	Macau	2,946
19	Iran[a]	20,650		44	Egypt	2,635
20	Hong Kong	20,151		45	Peru	2,589
21	Qatar	16,113		46	Botswana	1,940
22	Nigeria[a]	13,800		47	Bahrain	1,918
23	Brazil	13,620		48	Morocco	1,778
24	Finland	10,878		49	Ecuador	1,503
25	Angola	10,690		50	Bolivia	1,319

Largest deficits
$m, 2006

1	United States	-811,490		23	Iceland	-4,234
2	Spain	-106,344		24	Serbia	-3,966
3	United Kingdom	-77,550		25	Slovakia	-3,919
4	Italy	-47,312		26	Croatia	-3,220
5	Australia	-41,240		27	Lithuania	-3,218
6	Turkey	-32,774		28	Colombia	-3,057
7	Greece	-29,565		29	Estonia	-2,446
8	France	-28,310		30	Thailand	-2,175
9	Portugal	-18,281		31	Mexico	-2,008
10	South Africa	-16,487		32	Jordan	-1,909
11	Romania	-12,785		33	Kazakhstan	-1,795
12	Euro area (12)	-12,490		34	Ethiopia	-1,786
13	Poland	-11,084		35	Ukraine	-1,617
14	India	-9,415		36	Guatemala	-1,592
15	New Zealand	-9,381		37	Bahamas	-1,567
16	Ireland	-9,095		38	Belarus	-1,512
17	Hungary	-7,421		39	Lebanon	-1,451
18	Pakistan	-6,795		40	Tanzania	-1,442
19	Sudan	-5,110		41	Sri Lanka	-1,434
20	Bulgaria	-5,010		42	Georgia	-1,236
21	Czech Republic	-4,586		43	Bosnia	-1,233
22	Latvia	-4,522		44	Jamaica	-1,170

Largest surpluses as % of GDP
%, 2006

#	Country	Value	#	Country	Value
1	Kuwait	49.9	26	Hong Kong	10.6
2	Brunei	45.3	27	Luxembourg	10.5
3	Libya	44.1	28	Russia	9.6
4	Turkmenistan	31.9	29	Aruba	9.5
5	Qatar	30.6		Iran[a]	9.5
6	Saudi Arabia	28.4	31	China	9.4
7	United Arab Emirates	27.7	32	Netherlands	8.4
8	Singapore	27.5	33	Myanmar	8.0
9	Trinidad & Tobago	25.7	34	Sweden	7.4
10	Algeria	25.2	35	Zambia	6.9
11	Angola	23.7	36	Taiwan	6.8
12	Macau	20.8	37	Israel	5.7
13	Azerbaijan	18.7	38	Finland	5.2
14	Uzbekistan	18.6		Germany	5.2
15	Botswana	18.3		Suriname	5.2
16	Norway	17.4	41	Philippines	5.0
17	Malaysia	16.9	42	Equatorial Guinea	4.5
18	Namibia	15.2		Lesotho	4.5
19	Venezuela	14.9	44	Japan	3.9
20	Switzerland	14.4	45	Argentina	3.8
21	Oman	14.2	46	Swaziland	3.7
22	Iraq[a]	13.4	47	Chile	3.6
23	Bahrain	12.0		Ecuador	3.6
	Nigeria	12.0	49	Mongolia	3.5
25	Bolivia	11.8	50	Austria	3.2

Largest deficits as % of GDP
%, 2006

#	Country	Value	#	Country	Value
1	Liberia	-58.4		Moldova	-11.7
2	Burundi	-36.0	22	Tanzania	-11.3
3	West Bank and Gaza[b]	-27.3	23	Lithuania	-10.8
4	Iceland	-26.0	24	Romania	-10.5
5	Bahamas	-25.4	25	Burkina Faso[b]	-10.3
6	Fiji	-22.8	26	Bosnia	-10.1
7	Latvia	-22.5		Sierra Leone	-10.1
8	Nicaragua	-16.1	28	Senegal	-9.7
9	Georgia	-16.0	29	Greece	-9.6
10	Bulgaria	-15.9		Mauritius	-9.6
11	Laos[b]	-15.8	31	Portugal	-9.4
12	Estonia	-14.9	32	Mozambique	-9.3
13	Zimbabwe[a]	-14.5	33	Chad	-9.2
14	Kyrgyzstan	-14.3	34	New Zealand	-9.0
15	Gambia, The	-14.2	35	Madagascar	-8.7
16	Sudan	-13.6		Spain	-8.7
17	Jordan	-13.5	37	Niger	-8.4
18	Ethiopia	-13.4	38	Barbados	-8.1
19	Serbia	-12.4		Ghana	-8.1
20	Jamaica	-11.7		Turkey	-8.1

a Estimate.   b 2005

Inflation

Consumer price inflation

Highest, 2007, %

1	Zimbabwe	24,411.0
2	Congo-Kinshasa[a]	21.3
3	Yemen[b]	20.8
4	Myanmar[b]	20.0
5	Venezuela	18.7
6	Sri Lanka	17.5
7	Ethiopia	17.2
	Iran	17.2
9	Azerbaijan	16.7
10	United Arab Emirates	14.0
11	Qatar	13.8
12	Ukraine	12.8
13	Moldova	12.4
14	Guyana	12.3
15	Angola	12.2
16	Serbia[b]	11.7
	Sierra Leone	11.7
18	Suriname[b]	11.3
19	Nicaragua	11.1
20	Ghana[b]	10.9
21	Kazakhstan	10.8
22	Zambia	10.7

Lowest, 2007, %

1	Burkina Faso	-0.2
2	Japan	0.1
	Niger	0.1
4	Israel	0.5
5	Norway	0.7
	Switzerland	0.7
7	Cameroon	0.9
8	Togo	1.0
9	Benin	1.3
	Malta	1.3
11	Mali	1.4
12	France	1.5
13	Netherlands	1.6
14	Denmark	1.7
15	Belgium	1.8
	Italy	1.8
	Peru	1.8
18	Côte d'Ivoire	1.9
	Vanuatu[b]	1.9
20	Bahrain[b]	2.0
	Hong Kong	2.0
	Malaysia	2.0
	Morocco	2.0

Consumer price inflation, 2002–07

Highest average annual consumer price inflation, %

1	Zimbabwe	1,091.2
2	Angola	34.8
3	Venezuela	20.1
4	Haiti	19.4
5	Dominican Republic	18.1
6	Myanmar[d]	17.0
7	Ghana[d]	16.2
8	Zambia	15.4
9	Iran	14.7
10	Belarus	14.2
11	Yemen[d]	13.9
12	Suriname[d]	13.4
13	Turkey	12.9
14	Congo-Kinshasa[c]	12.5
15	Ethiopia	12.3
	Moldova	12.3
17	Serbia[d]	12.2
18	Nigeria	12.0
19	Malawi	11.6
20	Jamaica	11.4

Lowest average annual consumer price inflation, %

1	Japan	0.0
	Montenegro	0.0
3	Libya[d]	0.2
4	Hong Kong	0.4
5	Israel	0.8
6	Mali	0.9
	Switzerland	0.9
8	Maldives	1.1
	Singapore	1.1
	Taiwan	1.1
11	Finland	1.2
12	Niger	1.3
	Sweden	1.3
14	Guinea Bissau	1.4
15	Netherlands	1.5
	Norway	1.5
	Oman[d]	1.5
18	Saudi Arabia	1.6
19	Cameroon	1.7
	Denmark	1.7
	Gabon[d]	1.7
	Germany	1.7

a 2005 b 2006 c 2002–05 d 2002–06

Commodity prices

2007, % change on a year earlier		2000–07, % change	
1 Lead	100.8	1 Lead	467.2
2 Tin	65.6	2 Nickel	331.6
3 Palm oil	64.5	3 Copper	293.1
4 Wheat	57.2	4 Zinc	188.8
5 Nickel	53.9	5 Tin	166.7
6 Coconut oil	51.7	6 Palm oil	154.0
7 Soyabean	45.0	7 Gold	149.0
8 Soya oil	44.5	8 Wheat	145.6
9 Corn	43.2	9 Oil[a]	136.3
10 Soya meal	35.1	10 Soya oil	126.2
11 Wool (Aus)	26.4	11 Cocoa	119.5
12 Cocoa	22.7	12 Rubber	112.6
13 Gold	15.1	13 Coconut oil	100.5
14 Coffee	12.5	14 Corn	78.2
15 Cotton	10.2	15 Soyabeans	72.1
16 Oil[a]	8.6	16 Aluminium	70.3
17 Rice	7.6	17 Rice	60.1
18 Copper	5.8	18 Coffee	47.8
19 Hides	4.8	19 Lamb	43.0
20 Beef (US)	3.4	20 Beef (Aus)	41.2
21 Aluminium	2.8	21 Soya meal	40.0
22 Lamb	2.1	22 Wool (Aus)	35.4
23 Beef (Aus)	1.8	23 Beef (US)	29.8
24 Zinc	-0.3	24 Sugar	23.2
25 Rubber	-3.0	25 Hides	12.7
26 Wool (NZ)	-6.5	26 Cotton	7.4

The Economist's house-price indicators

Q4 2007[b], % change on a year earlier		1997–2007, % change	
1 Singapore	31.2	1 South Africa	395
2 Hong Kong	24.3	2 Ireland	227
3 Australia	12.3	3 United Kingdom	210
4 Belgium	11.4	4 Spain	190
5 Sweden	11.3	5 Australia	168
6 China	10.5	6 France	150
7 South Africa	9.1	7 Sweden	149
8 New Zealand	8.9	8 Belgium	142
9 Canada	6.0	9 Denmark	129
10 France	5.6	10 New Zealand	124
11 Italy	5.1	11 United States	104
12 Spain	4.8	12 Italy	102
13 United Kingdom	4.2	Netherlands	102
14 Netherlands	3.8	14 Canada	80
15 Denmark	2.1	15 Switzerland	19
16 Switzerland	2.0	16 Hong Kong	-29
17 Japan	-0.7	17 Japan	-32
18 Germany	-2.7		
19 Ireland	-7.3		
20 United States	-8.9		

a West Texas Intermediate.   b Or latest.

Energy

Largest producers
Million tonnnes oil equivalent, 2005

1	China	1,641		16	Algeria	175
2	United States	1,631		17	United Arab Emirates	168
3	Russia	1,185		18	South Africa	159
4	Saudi Arabia	577		19	Kuwait	146
5	India	419		20	France	137
6	Canada	401		21	Germany	135
7	Iran	304		22	Kazakhstan	122
8	Australia	271		23	Japan	100
9	Indonesia	263		24	Iraq	96
10	Mexico	259		25	Libya	95
11	Norway	234		26	Malaysia	94
12	Nigeria	232		27	Argentina	81
13	Venezuela	205			Ukraine	81
14	United Kingdom	204		29	Poland	79
15	Brazil	188		30	Egypt	76

Largest consumers
Million tonnnes oil equivalent, 2005

1	United States	2,340		16	Spain	145
2	China	1,717		17	Ukraine	143
3	Russia	647		18	Saudi Arabia	140
4	India	537		19	South Africa	128
5	Japan	531		20	Australia	122
6	Germany	345		21	Nigeria	104
7	France	276		22	Thailand	100
8	Canada	272		23	Poland	93
9	United Kingdom	234		24	Turkey	85
10	South Korea	214		25	Netherlands	82
11	Brazil	210		26	Pakistan	76
12	Italy	185		27	Argentina	64
13	Indonesia	180		28	Egypt	61
14	Mexico	177			Malaysia	61
15	Iran	163			Venezuela	61

Energy efficiency[a]

Most efficient			Least efficient		
GDP per unit of energy use, 2005			*GDP per unit of energy use, 2005*		
1	Hong Kong	13.5	1	Zimbabwe	0.2
2	Peru	12.7	2	Congo-Kinshasa	0.9
3	Botswana	11.6	3	Uzbekistan	1.1
4	Uruguay	10.6	4	Mozambique	1.4
5	Greece	10.5	5	Trinidad & Tobago	1.6
	Panama	10.5	6	Tanzania	1.8
7	Gabon	10.4		Ukraine	1.8
8	Ireland	10.3	8	Zambia	1.9
9	Costa Rica	9.9	9	Ethiopia	2.0
10	Congo-Brazzaville	9.8	10	Nigeria	2.1
11	Switzerland	9.6	11	Togo	2.3

a 2005 PPP$, per kg of oil equivalent.

Net energy importers
% of commercial energy use, 2005

Highest			Lowest	
1	Hong Kong	100	1 Congo-Brazzaville	-1,041
	Singapore	100	2 Norway	-627
3	Moldova	98	3 Angola	-614
4	Jordan	96	4 Gabon	-604
	Lebanon	96	5 Kuwait	-420
6	Morocco	93	6 Algeria	-404
7	Ireland	89	7 Libya	-399
	Israel	89	8 Oman	-327
9	Jamaica	87	9 Saudi Arabia	-311
	Portugal	87	10 Turkmenistan	-274
11	Belarus	86	11 United Arab Emirates	-258

Largest consumption per head
Kg of oil equivalent, 2005

1	United Arab Emirates	11,436	12	Oman	5,570
2	Kuwait	11,100	13	Belgium	5,407
3	Trinidad & Tobago	9,599	14	Netherlands	5,015
4	Canada	8,417	15	France	4,534
5	United States	7,893	16	Russia	4,517
6	Norway	6,948	17	South Korea	4,426
7	Singapore	6,933	18	Czech Republic	4,417
8	Finland	6,664	19	Germany	4,180
9	Saudi Arabia	6,068	20	Austria	4,174
10	Australia	5,978	21	Japan	4,152
11	Sweden	5,782	22	New Zealand	4,090

Sources of electricity
% of total, 2005

Oil			Gas		
1	Yemen	100.0	1	Turkmenistan	100.0
2	Benin	99.1	2	Trinidad and Tobago	99.5
3	Iraq	98.5	3	Moldova	98.1
4	Cuba	97.5	4	United Arab Emirates	97.9
5	Jamaica	96.6	5	Algeria	96.2

Hydropower			Nuclear power		
1	Paraguay	100.0	1	France	79.1
2	Mozambique	99.8	2	Lithuania	71.1
	Nepal	99.8	3	Slovakia	56.5
4	Congo-Brazzaville	99.7	4	Belgium	55.5
	Congo-Kinshasa	99.7	5	Ukraine	47.7

Coal		
1	Botswana	99.4
2	South Africa	94.1
3	Poland	93.4
4	Estonia	91.2
5	Australia	80.1

The business world

Global competitiveness, 2008

	Overall	Government	Infrastructure
1	United States	Singapore	United States
2	Singapore	Hong Kong	Switzerland
3	Hong Kong	Switzerland	Singapore
4	Switzerland	Denmark	Japan
5	Luxembourg	Australia	Sweden
6	Denmark	New Zealand	Germany
7	Australia	Ireland	Denmark
8	Canada	Canada	Canada
9	Sweden	Chile	Netherlands
10	Netherlands	Estonia	Norway
11	Norway	Sweden	France
12	Ireland	China	Finland
13	Taiwan	Finland	Austria
14	Austria	Luxembourg	Israel
15	Finland	Norway	Belgium
16	Germany	Taiwan	Australia
17	China	Netherlands	Taiwan
18	New Zealand	United States	Luxembourg
19	Malaysia	Malaysia	Hong Kong
20	Israel	Austria	United Kingdom
21	United Kingdom	Israel	South Korea
22	Japan	Thailand	New Zealand
23	Estonia	India	Ireland
24	Belgium	United Kingdom	Czech Republic
25	France	Jordan	Malaysia
26	Chile	Germany	Estonia
27	Thailand	Portugal	Hungary
28	Czech Republic	South Africa	Portugal
29	India	Bulgaria	Slovenia
30	Slovakia	Russia	Spain
31	South Korea	Slovakia	China
32	Slovenia	Peru	Lithuania
33	Spain	Czech Republic	Italy
34	Jordan	Spain	Jordan
35	Peru	Colombia	Greece
36	Lithuania	Lithuania	Slovakia
37	Portugal	South Korea	Poland
38	Hungary	Indonesia	Chile
39	Bulgaria	Japan	Thailand
40	Philippines	Mexico	Croatia
41	Colombia	Philippines	Bulgaria
42	Greece	Belgium	Turkey
43	Brazil	Slovenia	Romania
44	Poland	Turkey	Colombia

Notes: Overall competitiveness of 55 economies is calculated by combining four factors: economic performance, government efficiency, business efficiency and infrastructure. Column 1 is based on 331 criteria, using hard data and survey data. Column 2 measures government efficiency, looking at public finance, fiscal policy, institutional and societal frameworks and business legislation. Column 3 includes basic, technological and scientific infrastructure, health and environment, and education.

The business environment

		2008–12 score	2003–2007 score	2003–2007 ranking
1	Denmark	8.76	8.74	2
2	Finland	8.74	8.71	3
3	Singapore	8.73	8.84	1
4	Canada	8.71	8.64	5
5	Switzerland	8.68	8.67	4
6	Australia	8.65	8.20	14
7	Hong Kong	8.64	8.64	7
8	Netherlands	8.63	8.59	8
	Sweden	8.63	8.34	11
10	United States	8.60	8.64	6
11	Ireland	8.57	8.53	9
12	United Kingdom	8.56	8.52	10
13	Germany	8.48	8.13	15
14	New Zealand	8.29	8.20	13
15	Austria	8.26	8.00	16
16	Belgium	8.25	8.22	12
17	Norway	8.14	7.97	17
18	Taiwan	8.11	7.57	22
19	France	8.03	7.89	18
20	Chile	8.02	7.80	79
21	Estonia	7.86	7.79	20
22	Israel	7.85	7.18	25
23	Spain	7.77	7.61	21
24	South Korea	7.59	7.10	29
25	United Arab Emirates	7.57	7.24	24
26	Japan	7.54	7.13	26
27	Qatar	7.53	6.92	31
28	Czech Republic	7.51	7.12	28
29	Slovakia	7.44	6.96	30
30	Portugal	7.41	6.77	33
31	Bahrain	7.40	7.12	27
32	Malaysia	7.39	7.30	23
33	Slovenia	7.37	6.83	32
34	Mexico	7.17	6.71	37
35	Poland	7.12	6.74	35
36	Hungary	7.09	6.73	36
37	Cyprus	7.06	6.74	34
38	Latvia	7.05	6.65	40
39	Italy	7.02	6.58	41
	Lithuania	7.02	6.69	38
41	Brazil	6.98	6.51	42
42	South Africa	6.96	6.13	46
43	Thailand	6.88	6.66	39
44	Greece	6.80	6.44	43
45	Bulgaria	6.77	5.97	47
46	Romania	6.71	5.95	48

Note: Scores reflect the opportunities for, and hindrances to, the conduct of business, measured by countries' rankings in ten categories including market potential, tax and labour-market policies, infrastructure, skills and the political environment. Scores reflect average and forecast average over given date range.

Business creativity and research

Innovation index[a]
2007

1	United States	5.77	13	Netherlands	4.88
2	Switzerland	5.74	14	United Kingdom	4.79
3	Finland	5.67	15	Austria	4.76
4	Japan	5.64	16	Belgium	4.74
5	Israel	5.57	17	France	4.69
6	Sweden	5.53	18	Norway	4.60
7	Germany	5.46	19	Ireland	4.54
8	South Korea	5.36	20	Iceland	4.52
9	Taiwan	5.24	21	Malaysia	4.50
10	Denmark	5.11	22	Australia	4.41
11	Singapore	5.08	23	Hong Kong	4.34
12	Canada	4.90	24	Luxembourg	4.18

Technological readiness index[b]
2007

1	Sweden	5.87	13	Canada	5.34
2	Iceland	5.77	14	Israel	5.29
3	Switzerland	5.67	15	Taiwan	5.27
4	Netherlands	5.65		United Kingdom	5.27
5	Denmark	5.64	17	Australia	5.20
6	Hong Kong	5.48	18	Austria	5.17
7	Norway	5.46	19	Estonia	5.07
	South Korea	5.46	20	Japan	5.06
9	United States	5.43	21	Germany	5.05
10	Luxembourg	5.38	22	France	4.88
11	Finland	5.36	23	Belgium	4.82
	Singapore	5.36		New Zealand	4.82

Brain drain[c]

Highest, 2007			*Lowest, 2007*		
1	Guyana	1.5	1	United States	6.0
	Lesotho	1.5	2	Qatar	5.7
3	Zimbabwe	1.7	3	United Arab Emirates	5.6
4	Macedonia	2.0	4	Norway	5.5
	Nepal	2.0	5	Chile	5.4
	Serbia	2.0		Ireland	5.4
	Zambia	2.0		Kuwait	5.4
8	Bulgaria	2.1	8	Switzerland	5.3
	Burundi	2.1	9	Finland	5.2
	Moldova	2.1		Japan	5.2
	Senegal	2.1	11	Iceland	5.1

a The innovation index is a measure of the adoption of new technology, and the interaction between the business and science sectors. It includes measures of the investment into research institutions and protection of intellectual property rights.
b The technological readiness index measures the ability of the economy to adopt new technologies. It includes measures of ICT usage, the regulatory framework with regard to ICT, and the availability of new technology to business.
c Scores: 1=talented people leave for other countries, 7=they always remain in home country.

Total expenditure on R&D

% of GDP, 2005			*$bn, 2005*	
1	Israel	4.71	1 United States	312.5
2	Sweden	3.86	2 Japan	146.0
3	Finland	3.48	3 Germany	70.0
4	Japan	3.17	4 United Kingdom	54.8
5	South Korea	2.98	5 France	45.2
6	Switzerland	2.93	6 China	29.9
7	Iceland	2.83	7 South Korea	23.6
8	United States	2.67	8 Canada	22.4
9	United Kingdom	2.55	9 Italy	18.9
10	Taiwan	2.52	10 Sweden	13.8
11	Germany	2.51	11 Spain	12.5
12	Denmark	2.44	12 Australia	11.6
13	Austria	2.36	13 Netherlands	10.8
	Singapore	2.36	14 Switzerland	10.5
15	France	2.13	15 Taiwan	8.7
16	Canada	1.98	16 Russia	8.2
17	Australia	1.82	17 Brazil	7.3
	Belgium	1.82	18 Austria	7.2
19	Netherlands	1.78	19 Finland	6.8
20	Luxembourg	1.56	20 Belgium	6.7
21	Slovenia	1.49	21 Denmark	6.3
22	Norway	1.48	22 Israel	6.1
23	Czech Republic	1.42	23 Norway	4.5
24	China	1.33	24 India	3.7
25	Ireland	1.25	25 Mexico	2.8

Patents

No. of patents granted to residents			*No. of patents in force*	
Total, average 2003–05			*Per 100,000 people, 2005*	
1	Japan	110,714	1 Luxembourg	5,604
2	United States	80,875	2 Taiwan	1,230
3	South Korea	39,650	3 Switzerland	1,152
4	Taiwan	35,599	4 Sweden	1,136
5	Russia	19,699	5 Singapore	991
6	China	16,700	6 Japan	879
7	Germany	13,216	7 South Korea	874
8	Ukraine	9,303	8 Belgium	851
9	France	9,023	9 Ireland	831
10	United Kingdom	3,644	10 New Zealand	830
11	Sweden	2,071	11 United Kingdom	792
12	Spain	1,853	12 Netherlands	776
13	Netherlands	1,827	13 Finland	752
14	Finland	1,170	14 Denmark	701
15	Canada	1,057	15 United States	568
16	Austria	883	16 France	566
17	Poland	815	17 Spain	549
18	Romania	698	18 Germany	525
19	India	695	19 Australia	474
20	Switzerland	626	20 Canada	457

Business costs and FDI

Office occupation costs

Rent, taxes and operating expenses, $ per sq. metre, November 2007

1	London (West End), UK	3,540	13	Dubai, UAE	1,058
2	Mumbai, India	2,040	14	Edinburgh, UK	1,001
3	London (City), UK	1,946	15	Paris (La Défense), France	937
4	Moscow, Russia	1,946	16	Madrid, Spain	905
5	Tokyo (Inner Central), Japan	1,922	17	Oslo, Norway	852
6	Tokyo (Outer Central), Japan	1,663	18	Seoul, South Korea	835
7	Paris, France	1,372	19	Stockholm, Sweden	824
8	New Delhi, India	1,364	20	Zurich, Switzerland	806
9	Dublin, Ireland	1,223	21	Milan, Italy	785
10	Hong Kong	1,144	22	Warsaw, Poland	741
11	Singapore	1,102	23	Abu Dhabi, UAE	733
12	New York (Midtown), US	1,085	24	Frankfurt am Main, Germany	726

Employment costs

Pay, social security and other benefits, production worker, 2007, $ per hour

1	Norway	39.12	11	Canada	26.28
2	Denmark	36.90	12	Australia	26.04
3	Germany	33.49	13	France	25.63
4	Finland	33.01	14	United States	25.26
5	Netherlands	32.27	15	Ireland	23.98
6	Belgium	31.87	16	Italy	21.94
7	Switzerland	30.87	17	Japan	20.72
8	Austria	30.41	18	Spain	18.48
9	Sweden	29.97	19	New Zealand	14.44
10	United Kingdom	27.18	20	Singapore	8.55

Foreign direct investment[a]

	Inflow, 2006, $m			*Outflow, 2006, $m*	
1	United States	175,394	1	United States	216,614
2	United Kingdom	139,543	2	France	115,036
3	France	81,076	3	Spain	89,679
4	Belgium	71,997	4	Switzerland	81,505
5	China	69,468	5	United Kingdom	79,457
6	Canada	69,041	6	Germany	79,427
7	Hong Kong	42,892	7	Belgium	63,005
8	Germany	42,870	8	Japan	50,266
9	Italy	39,159	9	Canada	45,243
10	Luxembourg	29,309	10	Hong Kong	43,459
11	Russia	28,732	11	Italy	42,035
12	Sweden	27,231	12	Brazil	28,202
13	Switzerland	25,089	13	Sweden	24,600
14	Singapore	24,207	14	Netherlands	22,692
15	Australia	24,022	15	Australia	22,347
16	Turkey	20,120	16	Ireland	22,101
17	Spain	20,016	17	Russia	17,979
18	Mexico	19,037	18	China	16,130

a Investment in companies in a foreign country.

Business burdens and corruption

Number of days taken to register a new company

Highest, 2008		Lowest, 2008	
1 Suriname	694	1 Australia	2
2 Guinea-Bissau	233	2 Canada	3
3 Haiti	202	3 Belgium	4
4 Congo-Kinshasa	155	4 Iceland	5
5 Brazil	152	Singapore	5
6 Venezuela	141	6 Denmark	6
7 Equatorial Guinea	136	Turkey	6
8 Angola	119	United States	6
9 Brunei	116	9 Estonia	7
10 Botswana	108	France	7
11 Indonesia	105	Madagascar	7
12 Laos	103	Mauritius	7
13 Liberia	99	Portugal	7
Namibia	99	Puerto Rico	7
15 Zimbabwe	96	15 Jamaica	8

Corruption perceptions index[a]

2007, 10 = least corrupt

Lowest		Highest	
1 Denmark	9.4	1 Myanmar	1.4
Finland	9.4	Somalia	1.4
New Zealand	9.4	3 Iraq	1.5
4 Singapore	9.3	4 Haiti	1.6
Sweden	9.3	5 Uzbekistan	1.7
6 Iceland	9.2	6 Afghanistan	1.8
7 Netherlands	9.0	Chad	1.8
Switzerland	9.0	Sudan	1.8
9 Canada	8.7	9 Congo-Kinshasa	1.9
Norway	8.7	Equatorial Guinea	1.9
11 Australia	8.6	Guinea	1.9
12 Luxembourg	8.4	Laos	1.9
United Kingdom	8.4	13 Bangladesh	2.0
14 Hong Kong	8.3	Cambodia	2.0
15 Austria	8.1	Central African Rep	2.0
16 Germany	7.8	Papua New Guinea	2.0
17 Ireland	7.5	Turkmenistan	2.0
Japan	7.5	Venezuela	2.0

Business software piracy

% of software that is pirated, 2006

1 Armenia	95	Venezuela	86
2 Azerbaijan	94	8 Indonesia	85
Moldova	94	9 Algeria	84
4 Zimbabwe	91	Cameroon	84
5 Vietnam	88	Ukraine	84
6 Pakistan	86		

a This index ranks countries based on how much corruption is perceived by business people, academics and risk analysts to exist among politicians and public officials.

Life expectancy

Highest life expectancy

Years, 2005–10

1	Andorra[a]	83.5		Malta	79.4
2	Japan	82.6		United Kingdom	79.4
3	Hong Kong	82.2		Virgin Islands (US)	79.4
4	Iceland	81.8	28	Finland	79.3
5	Switzerland	81.7	29	Guadeloupe	79.2
6	Australia	81.2	30	Channel Islands	79.0
7	Spain	80.9		Cyprus	79.0
	Sweden	80.9	32	Ireland	78.9
9	Canada	80.7	33	Costa Rica	78.8
	France	80.7	34	Luxembourg	78.7
	Israel	80.7		Puerto Rico	78.7
	Macau	80.7		United Arab Emirates	78.7
13	Italy	80.5	37	Chile	78.6
14	Cayman Islands[a]	80.2		South Korea	78.6
	New Zealand	80.2	39	Cuba	78.3
	Norway	80.2		Denmark	78.3
17	Singapore	80.0	41	United States	78.2
18	Austria	79.8	42	Bermuda[a]	78.1
	Netherlands	79.8		Portugal	78.1
20	Faroe Islands[a]	79.5	44	Slovenia	77.9
	Greece	79.5	45	Kuwait	77.6
	Martinique	79.5		Taiwan[a]	77.6
23	Belgium	79.4	47	Barbados	77.3
	Germany	79.4	48	Brunei	77.1

Highest male life expectancy

Years, 2005–10

1	Andorra[a]	80.6	10	Canada	78.3
2	Iceland	80.2	11	New Zealand	78.2
3	Hong Kong	79.4	12	Singapore	78.0
4	Japan	79.0	13	Norway	77.8
	Switzerland	79.0	14	Spain	77.7
6	Australia	78.9	15	Cayman Islands[a]	77.6
7	Sweden	78.7	16	Italy	77.5
8	Israel	78.6		Netherlands	77.5
9	Macau	78.5	18	Malta	77.3

Highest female life expectancy

Years, 2005–10

1	Andorra[a]	86.6		Virgin Islands (US)	83.3
2	Japan	86.1	11	Sweden	83.0
3	Hong Kong	85.1	12	Canada	82.9
4	Spain	84.2		Cayman Islands[a]	82.9
	Switzerland	84.2		Faroe Islands[a]	82.9
6	France	84.1	15	Israel	82.8
7	Australia	83.6		Macau	82.8
8	Italy	83.5	17	Puerto Rico	82.7
9	Iceland	83.3	18	Austria	82.6

a 2007 estimate.

Lowest life expectancy

Years, 2005–10

1	Swaziland	39.6		26	Tanzania	52.5
2	Mozambique	42.1		27	Ethiopia	52.9
3	Zambia	42.4			Namibia	52.9
4	Lesotho	42.6		29	Kenya	54.1
	Sierra Leone	42.6		30	Mali	54.5
6	Angola	42.7		31	Congo-Brazzaville	55.3
7	Zimbabwe	43.5		32	Guinea	56.0
8	Afghanistan	43.8		33	Benin	56.7
9	Central African Rep	44.7			Gabon	56.7
10	Liberia	45.7		35	Niger	56.9
11	Rwanda	46.2		36	Papua New Guinea	57.2
12	Guinea-Bissau	46.4		37	Eritrea	58.0
13	Congo-Kinshasa	46.5		38	Togo	58.4
14	Nigeria	46.9		39	Sudan	58.6
15	Somalia	48.2		40	Gambia, The	59.4
16	Côte d'Ivoire	48.3			Madagascar	59.4
	Malawi	48.3		42	Iraq	59.5
18	South Africa	49.3		43	Cambodia	59.7
19	Burundi	49.6		44	Ghana	60.0
20	Cameroon	50.4		45	Timor-Leste	60.8
21	Botswana	50.7		46	Haiti	60.9
	Chad	50.7		47	Myanmar	62.1
23	Uganda	51.5		48	Yemen	62.7
24	Equatorial Guinea	51.6		49	Senegal	63.1
25	Burkina Faso	52.3		50	Turkmenistan	63.2

Lowest male life expectancy

Years, 2005–10

1	Swaziland	39.8		11	Liberia	44.8
2	Sierra Leone	41.0		12	Guinea-Bissau	44.9
3	Angola	41.2		13	Congo-Kinshasa	45.2
4	Mozambique	41.7		14	Nigeria	46.4
5	Zambia	42.1		15	Somalia	46.9
6	Lesotho	42.9		16	Côte d'Ivoire	47.5
7	Central African Rep	43.3		17	Burundi	48.1
8	Afghanistan	43.9			Malawi	48.1
9	Zimbabwe	44.1		19	South Africa	48.8
10	Rwanda	44.6		20	Chad	49.3

Lowest female life expectancy

Years, 2005–10

1	Swaziland	39.4		10	Liberia	46.6
2	Lesotho	42.3		11	Nigeria	47.3
3	Mozambique	42.4		12	Congo-Kinshasa	47.7
4	Zambia	42.5		13	Rwanda	47.8
5	Zimbabwe	42.7		14	Guinea-Bissau	47.9
6	Afghanistan	43.8		15	Malawi	48.4
7	Sierra Leone	44.2		16	Côte d'Ivoire	49.3
8	Angola	44.3		17	Somalia	49.4
9	Central African Rep	46.1		18	South Africa	49.7

Death rates and infant mortality

Highest death rates
Number of deaths per 1,000 population, 2005–10

1	Sierra Leone	22.1		48	Benin	11.2
2	Swaziland	21.2		49	Czech Republic	10.9
3	Angola	20.5		50	Germany	10.7
4	Afghanistan	19.9		51	Portugal	10.6
5	Mozambique	19.8		52	Italy	10.5
6	Lesotho	19.2		53	Gambia, The	10.4
7	Zambia	18.8		54	Denmark	10.3
8	Guinea-Bissau	18.4		55	Kazakhstan	10.1
9	Liberia	18.3			Sudan	10.1
10	Central African Rep	18.1			Sweden	10.1
	Congo-Kinshasa	18.1			Togo	10.1
12	Zimbabwe	17.9		59	Belgium	10.0
13	Rwanda	17.2			Poland	10.0
14	South Africa	17.0			Slovakia	10.0
15	Nigeria	16.8		62	Greece	9.9
16	Somalia	16.6			North Korea	9.9
17	Ukraine	16.4			Slovenia	9.9
18	Russia	16.2			United Kingdom	9.9
19	Burundi	15.6		66	Finland	9.7
20	Chad	15.4			Madagascar	9.7
	Côte d'Ivoire	15.4			Myanmar	9.7
22	Bulgaria	14.8		69	Armenia	9.6
	Equatorial Guinea	14.8			Montenegro	9.6
	Malawi	14.8			Papua New Guinea	9.6
25	Belarus	14.7		72	Bosnia	9.5
	Mali	14.7			Channel Islands	9.5
27	Burkina Faso	14.4		74	Austria	9.4
	Cameroon	14.4		75	Ghana	9.3
29	Estonia	14.3		76	Eritrea	9.2
30	Botswana	14.1			Haiti	9.2
31	Niger	13.8			Macedonia	9.2
32	Latvia	13.6			Uruguay	9.2
33	Uganda	13.4		80	Iraq	9.1
34	Hungary	13.2			Norway	9.1
35	Ethiopia	13.0		82	Cambodia	9.0
36	Tanzania	12.9			Japan	9.0
37	Moldova	12.5			Senegal	9.0
38	Namibia	12.4		85	France	8.9
	Romania	12.4			Timor-Leste	8.9
40	Lithuania	12.3		87	Spain	8.8
41	Croatia	12.1		88	Luxembourg	8.7
42	Guinea	11.9			Faroe Islands[a]	8.7
43	Georgia	11.8		90	Netherlands	8.6
	Kenya	11.8		91	Thailand	8.5
45	Gabon	11.7		92	India	8.2
46	Serbia	11.6			Turkmenistan	8.2
47	Congo-Brazzaville	11.4			United States	8.2

Note: Both death and, in particular, infant mortality rates can be underestimated in certain countries where not all deaths are officially recorded.   a 2007 estimate.

Highest infant mortality
Number of deaths per 1,000 live births, 2005–10

1	Sierra Leone	160.3	21	Equatorial Guinea	92.3
2	Afghanistan	157.0	22	Malawi	89.4
3	Liberia	132.5	23	Togo	88.6
4	Angola	131.9	24	Cameroon	87.5
5	Mali	128.5	25	Ethiopia	86.9
6	Chad	119.2	26	Iraq	81.5
7	Côte d'Ivoire	116.9	27	Uganda	76.9
8	Somalia	116.3	28	Turkmenistan	74.7
9	Congo-Kinshasa	113.5	29	Gambia, The	74.2
10	Guinea-Bissau	112.7	30	Tanzania	72.6
11	Rwanda	112.4	31	Azerbaijan	72.3
12	Niger	110.8	32	Swaziland	71.0
13	Nigeria	109.5	33	Congo-Brazzaville	70.3
14	Burkina Faso	104.4	34	Pakistan	67.5
15	Guinea	102.5	35	Timor-Leste	66.7
16	Burundi	99.4	36	Myanmar	66.0
17	Benin	98.0	37	Senegal	65.7
18	Central African Rep	96.8	38	Madagascar	65.5
19	Mozambique	95.9	39	Sudan	64.9
20	Zambia	92.7	40	Lesotho	64.6

Lowest death rates
No. deaths per 1,000 pop., 2005–10

1	United Arab Emirates	1.4
2	Kuwait	1.9
3	Qatar	2.4
4	Oman	2.7
5	Brunei	2.8
6	Bahrain	3.2
7	Syria	3.4
8	Saudi Arabia	3.7
	West Bank and Gaza	3.7
10	Belize	3.8
11	Jordan	3.9
12	Costa Rica	4.1
	Libya	4.1
14	Malaysia	4.5
15	Cape Verde	4.7
	Macau	4.7
	Nicaragua	4.7
18	Mexico	4.8
	Philippines	4.8
20	Algeria	4.9
21	Cayman Islands[a]	5.0
	Panama	5.0
23	Ecuador	5.1
	Venezuela	5.1
	Vietnam	5.1

Lowest infant mortality
No. deaths per 1,000 live births, 2005–10

1	Iceland	2.9
2	Singapore	3.0
3	Japan	3.2
	Sweden	3.2
5	Norway	3.3
6	Finland	3.7
	Hong Kong	3.7
8	Czech Republic	3.8
9	Andorra[a]	4.0
10	South Korea	4.1
	Switzerland	4.1
12	Belgium	4.2
	France	4.2
	Spain	4.2
15	Germany	4.3
16	Australia	4.4
	Austria	4.4
	Denmark	4.4
19	Luxembourg	4.5
20	Israel	4.7
	Netherlands	4.7
22	Canada	4.8
	Slovenia	4.8
	United Kingdom	4.8
25	Ireland	4.9

a 2007 estimate.

Death and disease

Diabetes

% of population aged 20–79, 2007

1	United Arab Emirates	19.5
2	Saudi Arabia	16.7
3	Kuwait	14.4
4	Oman	13.1
5	Trinidad & Tobago	11.5
6	Mauritius	11.1
7	Egypt	11.0
8	Malaysia	10.7
	Puerto Rico	10.7
10	Mexico	10.6
	Syria	10.6
12	Jamaica	10.3
13	Nicaragua	10.1
	Singapore	10.1
15	Jordan	9.8
16	Panama	9.7
17	Pakistan	9.6
18	Costa Rica	9.3
	Cuba	9.3

Cardiovascular disease

Deaths per 100,000 population, age standardised, 2002

1	Turkmenistan	844
2	Tajikistan	753
3	Kazakhstan	713
4	Afghanistan	706
5	Russia	688
6	Uzbekistan	663
7	Ukraine	637
8	Moldova	619
9	Azerbaijan	613
10	Kyrgyzstan	602
11	Belarus	592
12	Georgia	584
13	Somalia	580
14	Egypt	560
15	Bulgaria	554
16	Yemen	553
17	Turkey	542
18	Albania	537
19	Sierre Leone	515

Cancer

Deaths per 100,000 population, age standardised, 2002

1	Mongolia	306
2	Bolivia	256
3	Hungary	201
4	Sierra Leone	181
5	Poland	180
6	Angola	179
7	Czech Republic	177
8	Peru	175
9	Slovakia	170
	Uruguay	170
11	Liberia	169
	Niger	169
	South Korea	169
14	Croatia	167
	Denmark	167
	Kazakhstan	167
17	Mali	166
18	Burkina Faso	162
	Swaziland	162
20	Congo-Kinshasa	161
	Lithuania	161
22	Côte d'Ivoire	160
	Slovenia	160

Tuberculosis

Incidence per 100,000 population, 2006

1	Swaziland	1,155
2	South Africa	940
3	Namibia	767
4	Lesotho	635
5	Zimbabwe	557
6	Timor-Leste	556
7	Zambia	553
8	Botswana	551
9	Sierra Leone	517
10	Cambodia	500
11	Mozambique	443
12	Côte d'Ivoire	420
13	Congo-Brazzaville	403
14	Rwanda	397
15	Congo-Kinshasa	392
16	Togo	389
17	Kenya	384
18	Ethiopia	378
19	Malawi	377
20	Burundi	367
21	Uganda	355
22	Gabon	354
23	Central African Rep	345

Note: Statistics are not available for all countries. The number of cases diagnosed and reported depends on the quality of medical practice and administration and can be under-reported in a number of countries.

Measles immunisation

Lowest % of children aged
12–23 months, 2006

1	Chad	23
2	Central African Rep	35
3	Somalia	35
4	Niger	47
5	Angola	48
	Laos	48
7	Gabon	55
	Venezuela	55
9	Swaziland	57
10	Haiti	58
11	India	59
	Madagascar	59
13	Guinea-Bissau	60
14	Mauritania	62
	Nigeria	62
16	Ethiopia	63
	Namibia	63
18	Timor-Leste	64
19	Papua New Guinea	65
20	Congo-Brazzaville	66

DPT[a] immunisation

Lowest % of children aged
12–23 months, 2006

1	Chad	20
2	Somalia	35
3	Gabon	38
4	Niger	39
5	Central African Rep	40
6	Angola	44
7	Haiti	53
8	Nigeria	54
9	India	55
10	Laos	57
11	Madagascar	61
12	Sierra Leone	64
13	Timor-Leste	67
14	Mauritania	68
	Swaziland	68
16	Indonesia	70
17	Guinea	71
	Venezuela	71
19	Ethiopia	72
	Mozambique	72

HIV/AIDS

Prevalence among population
aged 15 and over, %, 2005

1	Swaziland	34.5
2	Botswana	23.6
3	Lesotho	22.7
4	Zimbabwe	19.2
5	Namibia	17.7
6	South Africa	16.6
7	Zambia	15.8
8	Mozambique	14.4
9	Malawi	12.5
10	Central African Rep	10.0
11	Gabon	6.8
12	Côte d'Ivoire	6.4
13	Uganda	6.3
14	Kenya	6.1
15	Tanzania	5.9
16	Cameroon	4.9
17	Congo-Brazzaville	4.7
18	Guinea-Bissau	3.5
	Nigeria	3.5
20	Haiti	3.4
21	Angola	3.3
22	Burundi	3.1
	Chad	3.1
	Rwanda	3.1

AIDS

Estimated deaths per 100,000
pop., 2005

1	Swaziland	1,550
2	Zimbabwe	1,384
3	Lesotho	1,282
4	Botswana	1,020
5	Zambia	840
6	Namibia	837
7	Mozambique	707
8	South Africa	675
9	Malawi	605
10	Central African Rep	594
11	Kenya	409
12	Tanzania	365
13	Côte d'Ivoire	358
14	Gabon	340
15	Uganda	316
16	Cameroon	282
17	Congo-Brazzaville	275
18	Rwanda	232
19	Bahamas	200
	Barbados	200
	Belize	200
	Equatorial Guinea	200
	Suriname	200

a Diptheria, pertussis and tetanus

Consumer goods ownership

TV

Colour TVs per 100 households, 2006

1	United Arab Emirates	99.7			Portugal	98.7
2	Taiwan	99.6		18	China	98.5
3	Hong Kong	99.5			Poland	98.5
	Ireland	99.5			United States	98.5
	Japan	99.5		21	Netherlands	98.3
	United Kingdom	99.5			Switzerland	98.3
7	Greece	99.4		23	Norway	98.2
	Singapore	99.4		24	Denmark	98.0
	Spain	99.4			New Zealand	98.0
10	South Korea	99.2		26	Germany	97.7
11	Kuwait	99.1		27	Czech Republic	97.5
12	Canada	99.0		28	Sweden	97.3
13	Australia	98.8		29	Saudi Arabia	97.2
	Belgium	98.8		30	Finland	96.9
15	Austria	98.7		31	Slovenia	96.7
	Hungary	98.7		32	Italy	96.6

Telephone

Telephone lines per 100 people, 2006

1	Bermuda	89.5		18	Andorra	51.3
2	Switzerland	66.9		19	Barbados	50.1
3	Germany	65.9		20	Malta	50.0
4	Canada	64.5		21	Ireland	49.9
5	Taiwan	63.6		22	South Korea	49.8
6	Iceland	63.5		23	Australia	48.8
	Virgin Islands (US)	63.5		24	Faroe Islands	48.7
8	Greenland	62.8		25	Cyprus	48.3
9	Sweden	59.5		26	Netherlands	46.6
10	Montenegro	58.9		27	Italy	46.3
11	United States	57.2		28	Spain	45.8
12	Denmark	56.9		29	Belgium	45.2
13	United Kingdom	56.2		30	Norway	44.3
14	France	55.8		31	New Zealand	44.1
15	Greece	55.4		32	Israel	43.9
16	Hong Kong	53.9		33	Austria	43.4
17	Luxembourg	52.4		34	Japan	43.0

CD player

CD players per 100 households, 2006

1	New Zealand	88.5		12	Austria	69.5
2	United Kingdom	88.4		13	Belgium	65.5
3	Denmark	88.1		14	Finland	63.8
	Norway	88.1		15	United States	61.3
5	Netherlands	87.0		16	Switzerland	59.2
6	Australia	85.5		17	Hong Kong	58.4
7	Germany	84.1		18	Singapore	56.0
8	Sweden	82.9		19	Portugal	42.6
9	Canada	81.5		20	Spain	42.1
10	Taiwan	70.6		21	Ireland	40.7
11	Japan	69.8		22	Peru	36.3

Computer

Computers per 100 people, 2006

1	Israel	122.1	25	Slovakia	35.8
2	Canada	87.6	26	Spain	27.7
3	Switzerland	86.5	27	Czech Republic	27.4
4	Netherlands	85.4	28	United Arab Emirates	25.6
5	Sweden	83.6	29	Latvia	24.6
6	United States	76.2	30	Poland	24.2
7	United Kingdom	75.8	31	Kuwait	23.7
8	Australia	75.7	32	Costa Rica	23.1
9	Denmark	69.6	33	Macedonia	22.2
10	Singapore	68.2	34	Malaysia	21.8
11	Japan	67.6	35	Croatia	19.9
12	Hong Kong	61.2	36	Lithuania	18.0
13	Austria	60.7	37	Mauritius	16.9
14	Germany	60.6	38	Brazil	16.1
15	Norway	59.4	39	Hungary	14.9
16	France	57.5	40	Chile	14.1
17	South Korea	53.2	41	Mexico	13.6
18	Ireland	52.8		Saudi Arabia	13.6
19	New Zealand	50.2		Uruguay	13.6
20	Finland	50.0	44	Mongolia	13.3
21	Estonia	48.3		Portugal	13.3
22	Slovenia	40.4	46	Romania	12.9
23	Belgium	37.7	47	Namibia	12.3
24	Italy	36.7	48	Russia	12.2

Mobile telephone

Subscribers per 100 people, 2006

1	Lithuania	138.1	25	Spain	106.4
2	Macau	137.4	26	Netherlands	106.0
3	Italy	135.1	27	Sweden	105.9
4	Hong Kong	132.7	28	Faroe Islands	105.7
5	Trinidad & Tobago	126.4		Russia	105.7
6	Estonia	125.2	30	Aruba	104.9
7	Bahrain	122.9	31	Germany	103.6
8	Israel	122.7	32	Cyprus	102.8
9	Czech Republic	121.5	33	Taiwan	102.0
10	United Arab Emirates	118.5	34	Hungary	99.0
11	Luxembourg	116.8		Switzerland	99.0
12	United Kingdom	116.6	36	Greece	98.6
13	Portugal	116.0	37	Australia	97.0
14	Austria	112.8	38	Andorra	96.9
15	Ireland	112.6	39	Croatia	96.5
16	Qatar	109.6	40	Poland	95.5
17	Singapore	109.3	41	Latvia	95.1
18	Iceland	108.7	42	Greenland	94.1
19	Norway	108.6	43	New Zealand	94.0
20	Finland	107.8	44	Jamaica	93.7
21	Bulgaria	107.6	45	Bermuda	93.3
22	Montenegro	107.3	46	Belgium	92.6
23	Denmark	107.0		Slovenia	92.6
24	Ukraine	106.5	48	Kuwait	91.5

Cinema and films

Cinema attendances

Total visits, m, 2006			Visits per head, 2006	
1	India	1,473.4	1	New Zealand	8.1
2	China	1,457.9	2	Australia	6.6
3	United States	1,447.7	3	United States	4.8
4	Indonesia	284.1	4	Iceland	4.7
5	France	188.7	5	Ireland	4.3
6	Mexico	169.2	6	Canada	4.1
7	Japan	164.3	7	Singapore	3.5
8	United Kingdom	156.6	8	France	3.1
9	Germany	136.7	9	Malta	2.8
10	Australia	135.6		Spain	2.8
11	Canada	135.1	11	Norway	2.6
12	Spain	121.7		United Kingdom	2.6
13	Italy	107.3	13	Luxembourg	2.5
14	Philippines	92.4	14	Belgium	2.3
15	Russia	89.8		Denmark	2.3
16	South Africa	65.8		Venezuela	2.3
17	Venezuela	63.7	17	Switzerland	2.2
18	Argentina	47.8	18	Austria	2.1
19	South Korea	47.5	19	Italy	1.8
20	Brazil	44.8	20	Germany	1.7
21	Turkey	34.9		Sweden	1.7
22	New Zealand	33.4	22	Mexico	1.6
23	Poland	32.0		Portugal	1.6
24	Belgium	23.8	24	Ecuador	1.5
25	Netherlands	22.5	25	Netherlands	1.4
26	Ecuador	20.1		Slovenia	1.4
27	Taiwan	18.5		South Africa	1.4
28	Ireland	17.9	28	Finland	1.3
29	Austria	17.3		India	1.3
30	Portugal	16.4		Indonesia	1.3
	Switzerland	16.4		Israel	1.3
32	Malaysia	16.3		Japan	1.3

Top Oscar winners

	Film	Awards	Nominations
1	Ben-Hur (1959)	11	12
	Titanic (1997)	11	14
	The Lord of the Rings: The Return of the King (2003)	11	11
4	West Side Story (1961)	10	11
5	Gigi (1958)	9	9
	The Last Emperor (1987)	9	9
	The English Patient (1996)	9	12
8	Gone with the Wind (1939)	8	13
	From Here to Eternity (1953)	8	13
	On the Waterfront (1954)	8	12
	My Fair Lady (1964)	8	12
	Cabaret[a] (1972)	8	10
	Gandhi (1982)	8	11
	Amadeus (1984)	8	11

a Did not win best picture award.

Music and the internet

Music sales

Total including downloads, $m, 2006		$ per head, 2006	
1 United States	6,497	1 United Kingdom	34.3
2 Japan	3,563	2 Japan	27.8
3 United Kingdom	2,054	3 Norway	26.1
4 Germany	1,411	4 Switzerland	24.9
5 France	1,126	5 United States	21.6
6 Canada	530	6 Australia	19.8
7 Australia	403	7 France	18.6
8 Italy	383	8 Germany	17.1
9 Spain	327	9 Canada	16.3
10 Mexico	236	10 Austria	15.9
11 Netherlands	233	11 Belgium	15.6
12 Brazil	222	12 Sweden	15.5
13 Russia	210	13 Netherlands	14.2
14 Switzerland	182	14 Spain	7.5
15 Belgium	162	15 Italy	6.6
16 South Africa	154	16 South Africa	3.2
17 South Korea	153	South Korea	3.2
18 Sweden	141	18 Mexico	2.2
19 Austria	130	19 Russia	1.5
20 Norway	120	20 Brazil	1.2

Internet hosts

By country, January 2008		Per 1,000 pop., January 2008	
1 United States[a]	291,214,772	1 United States[a]	967.5
2 Japan	36,803,719	2 Iceland	768.9
3 Germany	20,659,105	3 Finland	703.5
4 Italy	16,730,591	4 Netherlands	642.7
5 France	14,356,747	5 Denmark	603.0
6 China	13,113,985	6 Norway	592.4
7 Australia	10,707,139	7 Australia	524.9
8 Netherlands	10,540,083	8 Switzerland	453.2
9 Brazil	10,151,592	9 Estonia	434.3
10 Mexico	10,071,370	10 New Zealand	411.6
11 United Kingdom	7,727,550	11 Sweden	386.1
12 Poland	7,134,976	12 Belgium	347.9
13 Taiwan	5,121,607	13 Luxembourg	334.8
14 Canada	4,717,308	14 Andorra	328.4
15 Finland	3,728,551	15 Austria	315.8
16 Belgium	3,618,495	16 Ireland	297.1
17 Russia	3,577,635	17 Italy	288.0
18 Sweden	3,513,170	18 Japan	287.1
19 Switzerland	3,308,684	19 Greenland	252.3
20 Denmark	3,256,134	20 Germany	249.8
21 Argentina	3,128,975	21 France	236.5
22 Spain	3,085,513	22 Lithuania	230.5
23 Norway	2,725,031	23 Taiwan	224.6
24 Austria	2,589,316	24 Netherlands Antilles	215.0
25 India	2,584,572	25 Israel	205.6
26 Turkey	2,425,789	26 Czech Republic	205.2

a Includes all hosts ending ".com", ".net" and ".org", which exaggerates the numbers.

Drinking and smoking

Beer drinkers
Off-trade sales, litres per head of pop., 2006

1	Czech Republic	81.9
2	Venezuela	76.7
3	Australia	69.3
4	Germany	67.9
5	Austria	66.2
6	Finland	65.4
7	Russia	62.6
8	United States	62.5
9	Slovakia	62.4
10	Denmark	60.8
11	Hungary	60.4
12	New Zealand	55.0
13	Poland	54.5
14	Netherlands	54.3
15	Canada	52.7
16	Romania	51.3
17	Bulgaria	45.8
18	Mexico	45.3
19	Ukraine	43.5
20	Belgium	42.8
21	Sweden	41.0
22	Norway	40.3

Wine drinkers
Off-trade sales, litres per head of pop., 2006

1	Portugal	33.1
2	Switzerland	29.0
3	Italy	28.7
4	France	26.4
5	Denmark	26.2
6	Argentina	24.3
7	Hungary	23.7
8	Netherlands	22.6
9	Germany	21.1
10	Belgium	19.8
11	New Zealand	18.2
12	United Kingdom	17.7
13	Australia	17.6
14	Austria	17.2
15	Sweden	16.6
16	Ireland	14.9
17	Chile	13.6
18	Spain	12.7
19	Norway	12.3
20	Greece	11.8
21	Czech Republic	10.4
22	Finland	9.9

Alcoholic drinks
Off-trade sales, litres per head of pop., 2006

1	Australia	100.8
2	Czech Republic	97.7
3	Germany	96.4
4	Finland	93.3
5	Austria	90.2
6	Denmark	89.5
7	Hungary	88.3
8	Russia	86.4
9	New Zealand	81.3
10	Netherlands	80.4
	Venezuela	80.4
12	Slovakia	75.2
13	United States	74.8
14	Poland	69.4
15	Portugal	68.9
16	Canada	68.7
17	United Kingdom	66.0
18	Belgium	65.8
19	Sweden	64.1
20	Argentina	62.3
21	Romania	61.9
22	Switzerland	61.1
23	Norway	56.7

Smokers
Av. ann. consumption of cigarettes per head per day, 2007

1	Greece	8.2
2	Slovenia	7.0
	Ukraine	7.0
4	Bulgaria	6.7
5	Czech Republic	6.5
6	Macedonia	6.4
	Russia	6.4
8	Moldova	6.3
9	Spain	6.1
10	Bosnia	5.8
	Serbia	5.8
12	Armenia	5.7
13	Japan	5.6
14	Belarus	5.4
15	Latvia	5.2
16	Croatia	5.1
	Taiwan	5.1
18	Cyprus	5.0
	Lebanon	5.0
	Poland	5.0
21	Kazakhstan	4.9
22	Estonia	4.7
	South Korea	4.7

Crime and punishment

Murders

Per 100,000 pop., 2004

1	Ecuador	18.9
2	Swaziland	13.6
3	Mongolia	13.1
4	Suriname	10.4
5	Lithuania	9.3
6	Latvia	8.5
	Zimbabwe	8.5
8	Belarus	8.2
	Kyrgyzstan	8.2
10	Turkmenistan	8.1
11	Uganda	7.9
12	Ukraine	7.3
13	Estonia	6.8
	Sri Lanka	6.8
15	Moldova	6.7
16	Costa Rica	6.5
17	Georgia	6.1
18	Peru	5.7
	Uruguay	5.7
20	Philippines	4.5

Death row[a]

Population, latest available year

1	Pakistan	7,436
2	United States	3,246
3	Thailand	1,140
4	Kenya	946
5	Bangladesh	860
6	Burundi	533
7	Uganda	417
8	Tanzania	389
9	Nigeria	341
10	Sudan	300
11	Congo-Kinshasa[b]	200
12	Ghana	152
13	Taiwan[b]	100
14	Indonesia	90
15	South Korea	58
16	Cuba[b]	50
	Iraq[b]	50
18	Guatemala	34
19	Zimbabwe	26
20	Afghanistan[b]	25

Prisoners

Total prison pop., latest available year

1	United States	2,258,983
2	China	1,565,771
3	Russia	885,014
4	Brazil	419,551
5	India	358,368
6	Mexico	217,436
7	South Africa	166,267
8	Thailand	165,316
9	Iran	158,351
10	Ukraine	150,950
11	Indonesia	116,688
12	Vietnam	98,556
13	United Kingdom	91,300
14	Turkey[b]	90,000
15	Philippines	89,639
16	Pakistan	89,370
17	Poland	88,620
18	Bangladesh[b]	86,000
19	Rwanda[b]	82,000
20	Japan[b]	81,300
21	Germany	72,656
22	Spain	67,783
23	Ethiopia[b]	65,000
24	Colombia	63,603

Per 100,000 pop., latest available year

1	United States	751
2	Russia	627
3	Virgin Islands (US)	549
4	Cuba[b]	531
5	Turkmenistan[b]	489
6	Bahamas	462
7	Belize	460
8	Georgia	428
9	Belarus	426
10	Bermuda	394
11	Cayman Islands	391
12	Barbados	379
13	Kazakhstan	378
14	Netherlands Antilles	364
15	Puerto Rico	356
	Suriname	356
17	South Africa	348
18	Panama	337
19	Botswana	329
20	Ukraine	328
21	Aruba	324
22	Israel	305
23	Trinidad & Tobago	288
	United Arab Emirates	288

a Number of prisoners sentenced to death.   b Estimate.

Teenagers' health behaviour[a]

Computer use
% using a computer two or more hours every weekday

1	Netherlands	68	13	Finland	47
2	Iceland	60		Portugal	47
3	England	57	15	Luxembourg	46
	Estonia	57	16	Denmark	45
	Israel	57		Germany	45
6	Norway	55	18	Bulgaria	44
	Sweden	55		Latvia	44
8	Canada	54	20	Belgium (French)	39
	Wales	54		Slovakia	39
10	Belgium (Flemish)	52	22	Austria	38
11	Poland	51		Turkey	38
	Scotland	51		United States	38

Obesity[b]
% overweight or obese

Girls			Boys		
1	Malta	28	1	United States	33
2	United States	26	2	Malta	32
3	Greenland	23	3	Canada	25
4	Wales	18		Greece	25
5	Canada	14	5	Italy	23
6	Portugal	13	6	Iceland	22
7	Belgium (French)	12		Portugal	22
	Finland	12	8	Greenland	21
	Iceland	12		Wales	21
	Scotland	12	10	Slovenia	20
11	Germany	11	11	Austria	19
	Greece	11		Croatia	19
	Hungary	11		Finland	19
	Spain	11		Macedonia	19
15	Croatia	10		Spain	19
	Ireland	10	16	Bulgaria	18
	Italy	10	17	Hungary	17
	Netherlands	10		Israel	17
	Slovenia	10			

Smoking
% smoking every day

1	Greenland	34		Estonia	16
2	Bulgaria	26		Lithuania	16
3	Croatia	20	13	Germany	15
4	Austria	19		Ireland	15
	Latvia	19		Scotland	15
	Ukraine	19	16	France	14
7	Hungary	18		Italy	14
	Russia	18		Luxembourg	14
9	Finland	17		Netherlands	14
10	Czech Republic	16			

a WHO survey covering 41 countries in Europe and North America. Data is for 15 year-olds.
b According to body-mass index.

Cannabis
% using in past 12 months

Regular user (3–39 times)

1	Canada	14
2	United States	12
3	Spain	11
	Wales	11
5	Switzerland	10
6	France	9
	Netherlands	9
	Scotland	9
9	Belgium (Flemish)	8
	Czech Republic	8
	England	8
	Ireland	8
	Italy	8
	Luxembourg	8
15	Belgium (French)	7
	Estonia	7

Heavy user (40 times or more)

1	Canada	5
2	Spain	4
	Switzerland	4
4	Belgium (French)	3
	France	3
	Ireland	3
	Luxembourg	3
	Netherlands	3
	Scotland	3
	United States	3
	Wales	3
12	Croatia	2
	Czech Republic	2
	England	2
	Greenland	2

Alcohol
% drinking at least once a week

Beer

1	Ukraine	44
2	Czech Republic	28
3	Bulgaria	27
4	Italy	24
	Netherlands	24
	Denmark	24
7	England	23
	Croatia	23

Wine

1	Malta	23
2	Croatia	18
3	Italy	15
4	Hungary	13
	Slovenia	13
6	Austria	12

Spirits

1	Malta	26
2	Austria	20
3	Denmark	17
	Scotland	17
	Spain	17
6	Greece	15

Alcopops

1	Ukraine	22
2	Austria	21
3	England	19
	Wales	19
5	Malta	18
	Netherlands	18
7	Belgium (French)	17
	Scotland	17

Fighting
% involved in a physical fight at least once in the past 12 months

1	Malta	49		Macedonia	40
2	Belgium (French)	46	10	Lithuania	39
3	Greece	44		Ukraine	39
	Turkey	44	12	Netherlands	38
5	Slovakia	43	13	England	37
6	Czech Republic	41		Romania	37
	Ireland	41		Russia	37
8	Austria	40		Scotland	37

Environment

Environmental performance index[a], 2008

Highest			Lowest		
1	Switzerland	95.5	1	Niger	39.1
2	Norway	93.1	2	Angola	39.5
	Sweden	93.1	3	Sierra Leone	40.0
4	Finland	91.4	4	Mauritania	44.2
5	Costa Rica	90.5	5	Burkina Faso	44.3
6	Austria	89.4		Mali	44.3
7	New Zealand	88.9	7	Chad	45.9
8	Latvia	88.8	8	Congo-Kinshasa	47.3
9	Colombia	88.3	9	Guinea-Bissau	49.7
10	France	87.8		Yemen	49.7
11	Iceland	87.6	11	Guinea	51.3
12	Canada	86.6	12	Cambodia	53.8
13	Germany	86.3	13	Iraq	53.9
	Slovenia	86.3	14	Mozambique	53.9
15	United Kingdom	86.3	15	Madagascar	54.6
16	Lithuania	86.2	16	Burundi	54.7
17	Slovakia	86.0	17	Rwanda	54.9
18	Portugal	85.8	18	Zambia	55.1
19	Estonia	85.2	19	Sudan	55.5
20	Croatia	84.6	20	Central African Rep	56.0
21	Japan	84.5	21	Benin	56.1
22	Ecuador	84.4	22	Nigeria	56.2
23	Hungary	84.2	23	Bangladesh	58.0
	Italy	84.2	24	Pakistan	58.7
25	Albania	84.0	25	Ethiopia	58.8
	Denmark	84.0	26	Eritrea	59.4
	Malaysia	84.0	27	Malawi	59.9
28	Russia	83.9	28	India	60.3
29	Chile	83.4	29	Haiti	60.7
30	Luxembourg	83.1	30	Swaziland	61.3
	Panama	83.1	31	Uganda	61.6
	Spain	83.1	32	Togo	62.3
33	Dominican Republic	83.0	33	Senegal	62.8
34	Brazil	82.7	34	Cameroon	63.8
	Ireland	82.7	35	Tanzania	63.9
36	Uruguay	82.3	36	United Arab Emirates	64.0
37	Georgia	82.2	37	Kuwait	64.5
38	Argentina	81.8	38	Bolivia	64.7
39	United States	81.0	39	Papua New Guinea	64.8
40	Taiwan	80.8	40	Kazakhstan	65.0
41	Cuba	80.7		Uzbekistan	65.0
42	Belarus	80.5	42	China	65.1
	Poland	80.5		Myanmar	65.1
44	Greece	80.2	44	Côte d'Ivoire	65.2
45	Venezuela	80.0	45	Indonesia	66.2
46	Australia	79.8	46	Laos	66.3
	Mexico	79.8	47	Mongolia	68.1
48	Bosnia	79.7	48	Syria	68.2

a Based on a range of factors including environmental health, biodiversity, air
  pollution, water use, agricultural methods, tackling climate change.

Biggest emitters of carbon dioxide
Millions of tonnes, 2004

1	United States	6,044.0		26	Malaysia	177.4
2	China	5,005.7		27	Venezuela	172.5
3	Russia	1,523.6		28	Egypt	158.1
4	India	1,341.8		29	United Arab Emirates	149.1
5	Japan	1,256.8		30	Netherlands	141.9
6	Germany	808.0		31	Argentina	141.7
7	Canada	638.8		32	Uzbekistan	137.8
8	United Kingdom	586.7		33	Pakistan	125.6
9	South Korea	465.2		34	Czech Republic	116.9
10	Italy	449.5		35	Nigeria	113.9
11	Mexico	437.6		36	Belgium	100.6
12	South Africa	436.6		37	Kuwait	99.3
13	Iran	433.2		38	Vietnam	98.6
14	Indonesia	377.9		39	Greece	96.6
15	France	373.4		40	Romania	90.3
16	Brazil	331.5		41	Norway	87.5
17	Spain	330.2		42	Iraq	81.6
18	Ukraine	329.7		43	Philippines	80.4
19	Australia	326.5		44	North Korea	79.0
20	Saudi Arabia	308.1		45	Israel	71.2
21	Poland	307.0		46	Austria	69.8
22	Thailand	267.8		47	Syria	68.4
23	Turkey	225.9		48	Finland	65.7
24	Kazakhstan	200.1		49	Belarus	64.8
25	Algeria	193.8		50	Chile	62.4

Largest amount of carbon dioxide emitted per person
Tonnes, 2004

1	Kuwait	40.4		23	Belgium	9.7
2	United Arab Emirates	37.8			South Korea	9.7
3	Trinidad & Tobago	24.7		25	South Africa	9.4
4	United States	20.6		26	Greece	8.7
5	Canada	20.0			Netherlands	8.7
6	Norway	19.1			Turkmenistan	8.7
7	Australia	16.2		29	Austria	8.5
8	Estonia	14.0		30	Slovenia	8.1
9	Saudi Arabia	13.7		31	Poland	8.0
10	Kazakhstan	13.3		32	Italy	7.7
11	Finland	12.6			New Zealand	7.7
12	Oman	12.5			Spain	7.7
13	Singapore	12.3		35	Malaysia	7.0
14	Czech Republic	11.5		36	Ukraine	6.9
15	Russia	10.6		37	Slovakia	6.7
16	Israel	10.5		38	Belarus	6.6
17	Ireland	10.4			Serbia	6.6
18	Libya	10.3			Venezuela	6.6
19	Denmark	9.8		41	Iran	6.4
	Germany	9.8		42	France	6.2
	Japan	9.8		43	Algeria	6.0
	United Kingdom	9.8		44	Sweden	5.9

WORLD

Area	148,698,382 sq km	Capital	...
Arable as % of total land	11	Currency	...

People

Population	6,540.3m	Life expectancy: men	65.0 yrs
Pop. per sq km	43.9	women	69.5 yrs
Av. ann. growth		Adult literacy	82.4%
in pop. 2010–15	1.10%	Fertility rate (per woman)	2.5
Pop. under 15	28.3%	Urban population	48.7%
Pop. over 60	10.3%		per 1,000 pop.
No. of men per 100 women	102	Crude birth rate	21
Human Development Index	74.3	Crude death rate	8.6

The economy

GDP	$48.5trn	GDP per head	$7,410
Av. ann. growth in real		GDP per head in purchasing	
GDP 1996–2006	3.4%	power parity (USA=100)	21.0
		Economic freedom index	57.4

Origins of GDP

	% of total
Agriculture	3
Industry, of which:	28
manufacturing	18
Services	69

Components of GDP

	% of total
Private consumption	61
Public consumption	17
Investment	22
Exports	27
Imports	-27

Structure of employment[a]

	% of total		% of labour force
Agriculture	...	Unemployed 2006	6.0
Industry	...	Av. ann. rate 1995–2006	6.6
Services	...		

Energy

	m TOE		
Total output	11,441.1	Net energy imports as %	
Total consumption	11,209.7	of energy use	-2
Consumption per head,			
kg oil equivalent	1,796		

Inflation and finance

		av. ann. increase 2001–06	
Consumer price			
inflation 2007	3.8%	Narrow money (M1)[a]	8.4%
Av. ann. inflation 2002–07	3.6%	Broad money[a]	6.6%
LIBOR $ rate, 3-month, 2007	5.30%	Household saving rate, 2007[a]	4.3%

Trade

World exports

	$bn fob		$bn fob
Manufactures	7,825	Ores & metals	321
Fuels	1,043	Agricultural raw materials	214
Food	730		
		Total incl. others	**10,685**

Main export destinations		**Main origins of imports**	
	% of total		% of total
United States	15.1	China	9.8
Germany	7.4	Germany	8.8
China	5.9	United States	8.5
France	4.6	Japan	5.6
United Kingdom	4.5	France	4.0
Japan	4.4	United Kingdom	3.2

Balance of payments, reserves and aid, $bn

Visible exports fob	11,978	Overall balance	0
Visible imports fob	-11,845	Change in reserves	947
Trade balance	133	Level of reserves	
Invisibles inflows	5,766	end Dec.	5,643
Invisibles outflows	-5,736	No. months of import cover	4
Net transfers	-3	Official gold holdings, m oz	879.0
Current account balance	160	Aid given[b]	108.4
– as % of GDP	0.3	– as % of GDP[b]	0.30
Capital balance	-80		

Health and education

Health spending, % of GDP	10.1	Education spending, % of GDP	4.6
Doctors per 1,000 pop.	1.5	Enrolment, %: primary	106
Hospital beds per 1,000 pop.	...	secondary	65
Improved-water source access,		tertiary	24
% of pop.	83		

Society

No. of households	...	TVs per 100 households	...
Av. no. per household	...	Telephone lines per 100 pop.	19.6
Marriages per 1,000 pop.	...	Mobile telephone subscribers	
Divorces per 1,000 pop.	...	per 100 pop.	41.6
Cost of living, Dec. 2007		Computers per 100 pop.	10.6
New York = 100	...	Internet hosts per 1,000 pop.	82.8

a OECD countries.
b OECD, non-OECD Europe and Middle East countries.

EURO AREA[a]

Area	2,497,000 sq km	Capital	–
Arable as % of total land	25	Currency	Euro (€)

People

Population	311.5m	Life expectancy: men	76.5 yrs
Pop. per sq km	124.8	women	82.5 yrs
Av. ann. growth		Adult literacy	...
in pop. 2010–15	0.13%	Fertility rate (per woman)	1.5
Pop. under 15	16.0%	Urban population	76.2%
Pop. over 60	22.0%		per 1,000 pop.
No. of men per 100 women	96	Crude birth rate	9.3
Human Development Index	94.2	Crude death rate[b]	9.7

The economy

GDP	€8,429bn	GDP per head	$34,150
GDP	$10,636bn	GDP per head in purchasing	
Av. ann. growth in real		power parity (USA=100)	70.9
GDP 1997–2007	2.1%	Economic freedom index	68.1

Origins of GDP

	% of total
Agriculture	2
Industry, of which:	26
manufacturing	19
Services	72

Components of GDP

	% of total
Private consumption	58
Public consumption	21
Investment	20
Exports	37
Imports	-36

Structure of employment

	% of total		% of labour force
Agriculture	4.3	Unemployed 2006	8.2
Industry	27.8	Av. ann. rate 1995–2006	9.0
Services	69.5		

Energy

	m TOE		
Total output	450.5	Net energy imports as %	
Total consumption	1,244.4	of energy use	64
Consumption per head,			
kg oil equivalent	3,961		

Inflation and finance

		av. ann. increase 2001–06	
Consumer price			
inflation 2007	2.1%	Narrow money (M1)	10.5%
Av. ann. inflation 2002–07	2.1%	Broad money	7.4%
Interbank rate, 2007	3.86%	Household saving rate, 2007	9.9%

Exchange rates

	end 2007		December 2007
€ per $	0.68	Effective rates	2000 = 100
€ per SDR	1.07	– nominal	134.81
		– real	128.42

Trade[b]

Principal exports

	$bn fob
Machinery & transport equip.	652
Manufactures	385
Chemicals	237
Energy and raw materials	108
Food, drink & tobacco	75
Total incl. others	**1,754**

Principal imports

	$bn cif
Machinery & transport equip.	513
Energy & raw materials	501
Manufactures	446
Chemicals	138
Food, drink & tobacco	86
Total incl. others	**1,722**

Main export destinations

	% of total
United States	23.2
Switzerland	7.5
Russia	6.3
China	5.5
Japan	4.3

Main origins of imports

	% of total
China	14.4
United States	13.2
Russia	10.4
Norway	5.9
Japan	5.7

Balance of payments, reserves and aid, $bn

Visible exports fob	1,753.9	Overall balance	2.6
Visible imports fob	1,721.8	Change in reserves	51.6
Trade balance	32.1	Level of reserves	
Invisibles inflows	1,119.4	end Dec.	429.2
Invisibles outflows	1,067.3	No. months of import cover	1.8
Net transfers	-96.7	Official gold holdings, m oz	375.9
Current account balance	-12.5	Aid given	40.39
– as % of GDP	-0.1	– as % of GDP	0.38
Capital balance	155.5		

Health and education

Health spending, % of GDP	9.6	Education spending, % of GDP	5.3
Doctors per 1,000 pop.	4.0	Enrolment, %: primary	...
Hospital beds per 1,000 pop.	6.6	secondary	...
Improved-water source access, % of pop.	100	tertiary	...

Society

No. of households	130.5	Colour TVs per 100 households	97.0
Av. no. per household	2.39	Telephone lines per 100 pop.	53.2
Marriages per 1,000 pop.	4.6	Mobile telephone subscribers	
Divorces per 1,000 pop.	1.9	per 100 pop.	106.7
Cost of living, Dec. 2007		Computers per 100 pop.	47.6
New York = 100	...	Internet hosts per 1,000 pop.	255.8

---

a Data refer to the 12 EU members that had adopted the euro before December 31 2006: Austria, Belgium, France, Finland, Germany, Greece, Ireland, Italy, Luxembourg, Netherlands, Portugal and Spain.

b EU25 data, excluding intra-trade.

CANADA

Area[a]	9,970,610 sq km	Capital	Ottawa
Arable as % of total land	5	Currency	Canadian dollar (C$)

People

Population	32.6m	Life expectancy: men	78.3 yrs
Pop. per sq km	3.3	women	82.9 yrs
Av. ann. growth		Adult literacy	...
in pop. 2010–15	0.84%	Fertility rate (per woman)	1.5
Pop. under 15	17.6%	Urban population	81.1%
Pop. over 60	17.8%		per 1,000 pop.
No. of men per 100 women	98	Crude birth rate	11
Human Development Index	96.1	Crude death rate	7.4

The economy

GDP	C$1,442bn	GDP per head	$39,010
GDP	$1,272bn	GDP per head in purchasing	
Av. ann. growth in real		power parity (USA=100)	83.5
GDP 1997–2007	3.7%	Economic freedom index	80.2

Origins of GDP		Components of GDP	
	% of total		% of total
Agriculture	2.3	Private consumption	55.6
Industry, of which:	29.1	Public consumption	19.3
manufacturing & mining	20.4	Investment	22.0
Services	68.6	Exports	36.3
		Imports	-33.7

Structure of employment

	% of total		% of labour force
Agriculture	3	Unemployed 2006	6.3
Industry	22	Av. ann. rate 1995–2006	7.8
Services	75		

Energy

	m TOE		
Total output	401.3	Net energy imports as %	
Total consumption	272	of energy use	-48
Consumption per head,			
kg oil equivalent	8,417		

Inflation and finance

Consumer price		av. ann. increase 2001–06	
inflation 2007	2.1%	Narrow money (M1)	6.8%
Av. ann. inflation 2002–07	2.2%	Broad money	6.1%
Money market rate, 2007	4.34%	Household saving rate, 2007	2.4%

Exchange rates

	end 2007		December 2007
C$ per $	0.99	Effective rates	2000 = 100
C$ per SDR	1.56	– nominal	142.10
C$ per €	1.46	– real	138.10

Trade

Principal exports	$bn fob	Principal imports	$bn fob
Machinery & equipment	83.5	Machinery & equipment	101.1
Other industrial goods	82.8	Industrial goods	74.0
Energy products	76.5	Motor vehicles & parts	70.3
Motor vehicles and parts	72.8	Consumer goods	45.9
Total incl. others	**389.4**	Total incl. others	**348.7**

Main export destinations	% of total	Main origins of imports	% of total
United States	76.4	United States	65.0
United Kingdom	3.2	Japan	2.9
Japan	2.2	United Kingdom	2.4
EU25	5.4	EU25	7.8

Balance of payments, reserves and aid, $bn

Visible exports fob	401.8	Overall balance	0.8
Visible imports fob	-356.6	Change in reserves	2.0
Trade balance	45.1	Level of reserves	
Invisibles inflows	113.7	end Dec.	35.1
Invisibles outflows	-137.4	No. months of import cover	0.9
Net transfers	-0.6	Official gold holdings, m oz	0.1
Current account balance	20.8	Aid given	3.68
– as % of GDP	1.6	– as % of GDP	0.29
Capital balance	-15.5		

Health and education

Health spending, % of GDP	9.7	Education spending, % of GDP	...
Doctors per 1,000 pop.	2.2	Enrolment, %: primary	100
Hospital beds per 1,000 pop.	3.6	secondary	117
Improved-water source access,		tertiary	62
% of pop.	100		

Society

No. of households	12.3m	Colour TVs per 100 households	99.0
Av. no. per household	2.6	Telephone lines per 100 pop.	64.5
Marriages per 1,000 pop.	4.5	Mobile telephone subscribers	
Divorces per 1,000 pop.	2.2	per 100 pop.	57.6
Cost of living, Dec. 2007		Computers per 100 pop.	87.6
New York = 100	101	Internet hosts per 1,000 pop.	144.7

a Including freshwater.

CHINA

Area	9,560,900 sq km	Capital	Beijing
Arable as % of total land	15	Currency	Yuan

People

Population	1,323.6m	Life expectancy: men	71.3 yrs
Pop. per sq km	138.4	women	74.8 yrs
Av. ann. growth		Adult literacy	93.3%
in pop. 2010–15	0.54%	Fertility rate (per woman)	1.8
Pop. under 15	21.6%	Urban population	40.5%
Pop. over 60	11.0%		per 1,000 pop.
No. of men per 100 women	107	Crude birth rate	12
Human Development Index	77.7	Crude death rate	7.1

The economy

GDP	Yuan21,087bn	GDP per head	$2,000
GDP	$2,645bn	GDP per head in purchasing	
Av. ann. growth in real		power parity (USA=100)	10.6
GDP 1996–2006	10.5%	Economic freedom index	52.8

Origins of GDP		Components of GDP	
	% of total		% of total
Agriculture	11.7	Private consumption	36.4
Industry, of which:	48.9	Public consumption	13.7
manufacturing	...	Investment	40.9
Services	39.3	Exports	39.7
		Imports	-31.9

Structure of employment

	% of total		% of labour force
Agriculture	43	Unemployed 2005	4.2
Industry	25	Av. ann. rate 1995–2005	3.5
Services	32		

Energy

	m TOE		
Total output	1,640.9	Net energy imports as %	
Total consumption	1,717.2	of energy use	4
Consumption per head,			
kg oil equivalent	1,316		

Inflation and finance

Consumer price		av. ann. increase 2001–06	
inflation 2007	4.8%	Narrow money (M1)	15.4%
Av. ann. inflation 2002–07	2.6%	Broad money	17.2%
Deposit rate, 2007	4.14%		

Exchange rates

	end 2007		December 2007
Yuan per $	7.30	Effective rates	2000 = 100
Yuan per SDR	11.54	– nominal	99.28
Yuan per €	10.75	– real	101.12

Trade

Principal exports		Principal imports	
	$bn fob		*$bn cif*
Office equipment	134.5	Electrical machinery	174.8
Telecoms equipment	123.6	Petroleum products	84.1
Electrical machinery	101.7	Professional &	
Apparel & clothing	95.4	scientific instruments	48.6
Misc. manufactures	55.5	Metalliferous ores & scrap	44.0
		Office equipment	40.7
Total incl. others	**968.9**	Total incl. others	**791.5**

Main export destinations		Main origins of imports	
	% of total		*% of total*
United States	21.0	Japan	14.6
Hong Kong	16.0	South Korea	11.3
Japan	9.5	Taiwan	11.0
South Korea	4.6	United States	7.5
Germany	4.2	Germany	4.8

Balance of payments, reserves and debt, $bn

Visible exports fob	969.7	Change in reserves	249.3
Visible imports fob	-751.9	Level of reserves	
Trade balance	217.7	end Dec.	1,080.8
Invisibles inflows	143.2	No. months of import cover	14.5
Invisibles outflows	-140.4	Official gold holdings, m oz	19.3
Net transfers	29.2	Foreign debt	322.8
Current account balance	249.9	– as % of GDP	14
– as % of GDP	9.4	– as % of total exports	35
Capital balance	10.0	Debt service ratio	3
Overall balance	246.9		

Health and education

Health spending, % of GDP	4.7	Education spending, % of GDP	...
Doctors per 1,000 pop.	1.5	Enrolment, %: primary	111
Hospital beds per 1,000 pop.	2.4	secondary	76
Improved-water source access,		tertiary	22
% of pop.	77		

Society

No. of households	376.5m	Colour TVs per 100 households	98.5
Av. no. per household	3.5	Telephone lines per 100 pop.	27.8
Marriages per 1,000 pop.	6.3	Mobile telephone subscribers	
Divorces per 1,000 pop.	1.4	per 100 pop.	34.8
Cost of living, Dec. 2007		Computers per 100 pop.	4.3
New York = 100	82	Internet hosts per 1,000 pop.	9.9

Note: Data excludes Special Administrative Regions ie, Hong Kong and Macau.

FRANCE

Area	543,965 sq km	Capital	Paris
Arable as % of total land	34	Currency	Euro (€)

People

Population	60.7m	Life expectancy: men	77.1 yrs
Pop. per sq km	111.6	women	84.1 yrs
Av. ann. growth		Adult literacy	...
in pop. 2010–15	0.39%	Fertility rate (per woman)	1.9
Pop. under 15	18.4%	Urban population	76.7%
Pop. over 60	20.8%		per 1,000 pop.
No. of men per 100 women	95	Crude birth rate	13
Human Development Index	95.2	Crude death rate	8.9

The economy

GDP	€1,792bn	GDP per head	$37,040
GDP	$2,248bn	GDP per head in purchasing	
Av. ann. growth in real		power parity (USA=100)	72.8
GDP 1997–2007	2.5%	Economic freedom index	65.4

Origins of GDP		Components of GDP	
	% of total		% of total
Agriculture	2.0	Private consumption	56.7
Industry, of which:	20.8	Public consumption	23.6
manufacturing	...	Investment	20.5
Services	77.2	Exports	26.9
		Imports	-28.3

Structure of employment

	% of total		% of labour force
Agriculture	2	Unemployed 2005	9.8
Industry	24	Av. ann. rate 1995–2005	10.6
Services	74		

Energy

	m TOE		
Total output	136.9	Net energy imports as %	
Total consumption	27.6	of energy use	50
Consumption per head,			
kg oil equivalent	4,534		

Inflation and finance

Consumer price		av. ann. increase 2001–06	
inflation 2007	1.5%	Euro area:	
Av. ann. inflation 2002–07	1.8%	Narrow money (M1)	10.5%
Deposit rate, households, 2007	3.69%	Broad money	7.4%
		Household saving rate, 2007	13.1%

Exchange rates

	end 2007		December 2007
€ per $	0.68	Effective rates	2000 = 100
€ per SDR	1.07	– nominal	113.60
		– real	110.80

Trade

Principal exports	$bn fob	Principal imports	$bn cif
Intermediate goods	148.8	Intermediate goods	157.9
Capital goods	118.3	Capital goods	110.8
Consumer goods	73.6	Consumer goods	84.0
Motor vehicles & other		Energy	80.0
transport equipment	65.1	Motor vehicles & other	
Food & drink	40.9	transport equipment	56.9
Total incl. others	**482.6**	Total incl. others	**535.3**

Main export destinations	% of total	Main origins of imports	% of total
Germany	14.5	Germany	16.2
Spain	9.9	Belgium-Luxembourg	8.7
Italy	9.1	Italy	8.5
United Kingdom	8.5	Spain	6.9
Belgium-Luxembourg	7.8	United Kingdom	6.8
EU25	68.3	EU25	64.6

Balance of payments, reserves and aid, $bn

Visible exports fob	483.1	Overall balance	11.8
Visible imports fob	-520.8	Change in reserves	23.9
Trade balance	-37.7	Level of reserves	
Invisibles inflows	304.6	end Dec.	98.2
Invisibles outflows	-267.7	No. months of import cover	1.5
Net transfers	-27.5	Official gold holdings, m oz	87.4
Current account balance	-28.3	Aid given	10.60
– as % of GDP	-1.3	– as % of GDP	0.47
Capital balance	87.8		

Health and education

Health spending, % of GDP	11.1	Education spending, % of GDP	5.7
Doctors per 1,000 pop.	3.4	Enrolment, %: primary	110
Hospital beds per 1,000 pop.	7.5	secondary	114
Improved-water source access,		tertiary	56
% of pop.	100		

Society

No. of households	25.5m	Colour TVs per 100 households	95.3
Av. no. per household	2.4	Telephone lines per 100 pop.	55.8
Marriages per 1,000 pop.	4.1	Mobile telephone subscribers	
Divorces per 1,000 pop.	2.2	per 100 pop.	85.1
Cost of living, Dec. 2007		Computers per 100 pop.	57.5
New York = 100	141	Internet hosts per 1,000 pop.	236.5

GERMANY

Area	357,868 sq km	Capital	Berlin
Arable as % of total land	34	Currency	Euro (€)

People

Population	82.7m	Life expectancy: men	76.5 yrs
Pop. per sq km	231.0	women	82.1 yrs
Av. ann. growth		Adult literacy	...
in pop. 2010–15	-0.13%	Fertility rate (per woman)	1.4
Pop. under 15	14.4%	Urban population	88.5%
Pop. over 60	25.1%		per 1,000 pop.
No. of men per 100 women	96	Crude birth rate	8
Human Development Index	93.5	Crude death rate	10.7

The economy

GDP	€2,309bn	GDP per head	$35,030
GDP	$2,897bn	GDP per head in purchasing	
Av. ann. growth in real		power parity (USA=100)	73.5
GDP 1997–2007	1.7%	Economic freedom index	71.2

Origins of GDP		Components of GDP	
	% of total		% of total
Agriculture	0.9	Private consumption	58.5
Industry, of which:	29.4	Public consumption	18.3
manufacturing	...	Investment	18.0
Services	69.8	Exports	45.1
		Imports	-39.6

Structure of employment

	% of total		% of labour force
Agriculture	2	Unemployed 2006	10.3
Industry	30	Av. ann. rate 1995–2006	9.3
Services	68		

Energy

	m TOE		
Total output	134.5	Net energy imports as %	
Total consumption	344.7	of energy use	61
Consumption per head,			
kg oil equivalent	4,180		

Inflation and finance

Consumer price		av. ann. increase 2001–06	
inflation 2007	2.1%	Euro area:	
Av. ann. inflation 2002–07	1.7%	Narrow money (M1)	10.5%
Deposit rate, households, 2007	3.61%	Broad money	7.4%
		Household saving rate, 2007	11.1%

Exchange rates

	end 2007		December 2007
€ per $	0.68	Effective rates	2000 = 100
€ per SDR	1.07	– nominal	116.30
		– real	110.10

Trade

Principal exports		Principal imports	
	$bn fob		*$bn cif*
Road vehicles	210.4	Computer technology	105.0
Machinery	159.5	Fuels	97.1
Chemicals	148.0	Chemicals	86.9
Computer equipment	125.6	Road vehicles	73.8
		Machinery	52.9
Total incl. others	**1,121.7**	Total incl. others	**921.7**

Main export destinations		Main origins of imports	
	% of total		*% of total*
France	9.6	Netherlands	11.5
United States	8.5	France	8.6
United Kingdom	7.2	Belgium	7.5
Italy	6.7	United Kingdom	5.9
Netherlands	6.2	China	5.8
Belgium	5.5	Italy	5.4
Austria	5.4	United States	5.0

Balance of payments, reserves and aid, $bn

Visible exports fob	1,131.3	Overall balance	-3.7
Visible imports fob	-934.1	Change in reserves	10.0
Trade balance	197.2	Level of reserves	
Invisibles inflows	409.1	end Dec.	111.6
Invisibles outflows	-422.2	No. months of import cover	1.0
Net transfers	-33.3	Official gold holdings, m oz	110.0
Current account balance	150.8	Aid given	10.43
– as % of GDP	5.2	– as % of GDP	0.36
Capital balance	-179.5		

Health and education

Health spending, % of GDP	10.7	Education spending, % of GDP	4.6
Doctors per 1,000 pop.	3.4	Enrolment, %: primary	101
Hospital beds per 1,000 pop.	8.4	secondary	100
Improved-water source access,		tertiary	46
% of pop.	100		

Society

No. of households	39.4m	Colour TVs per 100 households	97.7
Av. no. per household	2.1	Telephone lines per 100 pop.	65.9
Marriages per 1,000 pop.	4.8	Mobile telephone subscribers	
Divorces per 1,000 pop.	2.8	per 100 pop.	103.6
Cost of living, Dec. 2007		Computers per 100 pop.	60.6
New York = 100	115	Internet hosts per 1,000 pop.	249.8

INDIA

Area	3,287,263 sq km	Capital	New Delhi
Arable as % of total land	54	Currency	Indian rupee (Rs)

People

Population	1,119.5m	Life expectancy: men	63.2 yrs
Pop. per sq km	340.6	women	66.4 yrs
Av. ann. growth		Adult literacy	66.0%
in pop. 2010–15	1.31%	Fertility rate (per woman)	2.6
Pop. under 15	33.0%	Urban population	28.7%
Pop. over 60	7.1%		per 1,000 pop.
No. of men per 100 women	107	Crude birth rate	24
Human Development Index	61.9	Crude death rate	8.2

The economy

GDP	Rs41,257bn	GDP per head	$810
GDP	$912bn	GDP per head in purchasing	
Av. ann. growth in real		power parity (USA=100)	5.6
GDP 1997–2007	7.8%	Economic freedom index	54.2

Origins of GDP[a]

	% of total
Agriculture	18.3
Industry, of which:	28.3
manufacturing	16.1
Services	52.4

Components of GDP[a]

	% of total
Private consumption	55.8
Public consumption	10.3
Investment	32.5
Exports	22.1
Imports	-25.1

Structure of employment

	% of total		% of labour force
Agriculture	...	Unemployed 2004	5.0
Industry	...	Av. ann. rate 1995–2004	3.3
Services	...		

Energy

	m TOE		
Total output	419	Net energy imports as %	
Total consumption	537.3	of energy use	22
Consumption per head,			
kg oil equivalent	491		

Inflation and finance

		av. ann. increase 2001–06	
Consumer price			
inflation 2007	6.4%	Narrow money (M1)	17.5%
Av. ann. inflation 2002–07	4.8%	Broad money	16.7%
Lending rate, 2007	13.02%		

Exchange rates

	end 2007		December 2007
Rs per $	39.42	Effective rates	2000 = 100
Rs per SDR	62.29	– nominal	...
Rs per €	56.03	– real	...

Trade

Principal exports[a]	$bn fob	Principal imports[a]	$bn cif
Engineering goods	26.2	Petroleum & products	57.1
Petroleum & products	18.6	Capital goods	32.7
Textiles	16.1	Electronic goods	15.9
Gems & jewellery	15.6	Gold & silver	14.6
Agricultural goods	11.2	Gems	7.8
Total incl. others	**126.3**	Total incl. others	**190.6**

Main export destinations	% of total	Main origins of imports	% of total
United States	19.1	China	7.3
China	9.4	United States	6.5
United Arab Emirates	8.4	Belgium	5.2
United Kingdom	4.9	Singapore	4.8

Balance of payments, reserves and debt, $bn

Visible exports fob	123.6	Change in reserves	40.2
Visible imports fob	-166.7	Level of reserves	
Trade balance	-43.1	end Dec.	178.1
Invisibles inflows	83.1	No. months of import cover	8.8
Invisibles outflows	-75.6	Official gold holdings, m oz	11.5
Net transfers	26.1	Foreign debt	153.1
Current account balance	-9.4	– as % of GDP	15
– as % of GDP	-1.0	– as % of total exports	63
Capital balance	37.8	Debt service ratio	8
Overall balance	23.7		

Health and education

Health spending, % of GDP	5.0	Education spending, % of GDP	3.2
Doctors per 1,000 pop.	0.6	Enrolment, %: primary	112
Hospital beds per 1,000 pop.	0.9	secondary	54
Improved-water source access,		tertiary	11
% of pop.	86		

Society

No. of households	209.9m	Colour TVs per 100 households	73.0
Av. no. per household	5.4	Telephone lines per 100 pop.	3.6
Marriages per 1,000 pop.	...	Mobile telephone subscribers	
Divorces per 1,000 pop.	...	per 100 pop.	14.8
Cost of living, Dec. 2007		Computers per 100 pop.	1.6
New York = 100	51	Internet hosts per 1,000 pop.	2.3

a Year ending March 31, 2007.

ITALY

Area	301,245 sq km	Capital	Rome
Arable as % of total land	26	Currency	Euro (€)

People

Population	58.1m	Life expectancy: men	77.5 yrs
Pop. per sq km	192.9	women	83.5 yrs
Av. ann. growth		Adult literacy	98.4%
in pop. 2010–15	-0.01%	Fertility rate (per woman)	1.4
Pop. under 15	14.0%	Urban population	67.5%
Pop. over 60	25.3%		per 1,000 pop.
No. of men per 100 women	94	Crude birth rate	10
Human Development Index	94.1	Crude death rate	10.5

The economy

GDP	€1,475bn	GDP per head	$31,860
GDP	$1,851bn	GDP per head in purchasing	
Av. ann. growth in real		power parity (USA=100)	66.1
GDP 1997–2007	1.6%	Economic freedom index	62.5

Origins of GDP

	% of total
Agriculture	1.9
Industry, of which:	28.9
manufacturing	...
Services	69.2

Components of GDP

	% of total
Private consumption	58.8
Public consumption	20.6
Investment	21.0
Exports	27.8
Imports	-28.6

Structure of employment

	% of total		% of labour force
Agriculture	4	Unemployed 2006	6.8
Industry	31	Av. ann. rate 1995–2006	9.8
Services	65		

Energy

	m TOE		
Total output	27.6	Net energy imports as %	
Total consumption	185.2	of energy use	85
Consumption per head,			
kg oil equivalent	3,160		

Inflation and finance

Consumer price		av. ann. increase 2001–06	
inflation 2007	1.8%	Euro area:	
Av. ann. inflation 2002–07	2.2%	Narrow money (M1)	10.5%
Money market rate, 2007	4.29%	Broad money	7.4%
		Household saving rate, 2007	6.8%

Exchange rates

	end 2007		December 2007
€ per $	0.68	Effective rates	2000 = 100
€ per SDR	1.07	– nominal	115.90
		– real	113.70

Trade

Principal exports

	$bn fob
Engineering products	144.6
Transport equipment	55.9
Chemicals	46.6
Textiles & clothing	38.0
Food, drink & tobacco	25.8
Total incl. others	**417.4**

Principal imports

	$bn cif
Engineering products	90.9
Energy products	70.3
Chemicals	64.6
Transport equipment	64.5
Food, drink & tobacco	31.4
Total incl. others	**441.7**

Main export destinations

	% of total
Germany	12.9
France	11.4
Spain	7.4
United States	6.8
United Kingdom	5.8
EU25	60.1

Main origins of imports

	% of total
Germany	16.9
France	9.0
Netherlands	5.5
Belgium	4.3
United States	3.0
EU25	57.0

Balance of payments, reserves and aid, $bn

Visible exports fob	417.1	Overall balance	-0.6
Visible imports fob	-428.7	Change in reserves	9.8
Trade balance	-11.7	Level of reserves	
Invisibles inflows	170.9	end Dec.	75.8
Invisibles outflows	-189.9	No. months of import cover	1.5
Net transfers	-16.7	Official gold holdings, m oz	78.8
Current account balance	-47.3	Aid given	3.64
– as % of GDP	-2.6	– as % of GDP	0.20
Capital balance	46.0		

Health and education

Health spending, % of GDP	8.9	Education spending, % of GDP	4.5
Doctors per 1,000 pop.	3.7	Enrolment, %: primary	103
Hospital beds per 1,000 pop.	4.0	secondary	100
Improved-water source access,		tertiary	67
% of pop.	...		

Society

No. of households	22.6m	Colour TVs per 100 households	96.6
Av. no. per household	2.6	Telephone lines per 100 pop.	46.3
Marriages per 1,000 pop.	4.5	Mobile telephone subscribers	
Divorces per 1,000 pop.	0.8	per 100 pop.	135.1
Cost of living, Dec. 2007		Computers per 100 pop.	36.7
New York = 100	105	Internet hosts per 1,000 pop.	288.0

JAPAN

Area	377,727 sq km	Capital	Tokyo
Arable as % of total land	12	Currency	Yen (¥)

People

Population	128.2m	Life expectancy: men	79.0 yrs
Pop. per sq km	339.4	women	86.1 yrs
Av. ann. growth		Adult literacy	...
in pop. 2010–15	-0.18%	Fertility rate (per woman)	1.3
Pop. under 15	13.9%	Urban population	65.7%
Pop. over 60	26.4%		per 1,000 pop.
No. of men per 100 women	95	Crude birth rate	9
Human Development Index	95.3	Crude death rate	9.0

The economy

GDP	¥508trn	GDP per head	$34,080
GDP	$4,368bn	GDP per head in purchasing	
Av. ann. growth in real		power parity (USA=100)	72.7
GDP 1997–2007	1.3%	Economic freedom index	72.5

Origins of GDPª		Components of GDP	
	% of total		% of total
Agriculture	1.5	Private consumption	57.1
Industry, of which:	26.9	Public consumption	17.7
manufacturing	...	Investment	23.5
Services	71.6	Exports	16.1
		Imports	-14.8

Structure of employment

	% of total		% of labour force
Agriculture	4	Unemployed 2006	4.1
Industry	28	Av. ann. rate 1995–2006	4.4
Services	68		

Energy

	m TOE		
Total output	99.8	Net energy imports as %	
Total consumption	530.5	of energy use	81
Consumption per head,			
kg oil equivalent	4,152		

Inflation and finance

Consumer price		av. ann. increase 2001–06	
inflation 2007	0.1%	Narrow money (M1)	7.1%
Av. ann. inflation 2002–07	0.0%	Broad money	0.4%
Money market rate, 2007	0.47%	Household saving rate, 2007	3.2%

Exchange rates

	end 2007		December 2007
¥ per $	114.00	Effective rates	2000 = 100
¥ per SDR	180.15	– nominal	82.40
¥ per €	167.82	– real	67.10

Trade

Principal exports

	$bn fob
Transport machinery	156.8
Electrical equipment	138.2
Non-electrical machinery	127.3
Chemicals	58.4
Metals	30.0
Total incl. others	**646.4**

Principal imports

	$bn cif
Mineral fuels	160.3
Electrical machinery	138.2
General machinery	127.3
Food	49.0
Chemicals	42.1
Total incl. others	**578.8**

Main export destinations

	% of total
United States	22.5
China	14.3
South Korea	7.8
Taiwan	6.8
Hong Kong	5.6

Main origins of imports

	% of total
China	20.5
United States	11.8
Saudi Arabia	6.4
United Arab Emirates	5.5
Australia	4.8

Balance of payments, reserves and aid, $bn

Visible exports fob	615.8	Overall balance	32.0
Visible imports fob	-534.5	Change in reserves	48.4
Trade balance	81.3	Level of reserves	
Invisibles inflows	283.1	end Dec.	895.3
Invisibles outflows	-183.2	No. months of import cover	15.0
Net transfers	-16.7	Official gold holdings, m oz	24.6
Current account balance	170.5	Aid given	11.19
– as % of GDP	3.9	– as % of GDP	0.26
Capital balance	-107.2		

Health and education

Health spending, % of GDP	8.2	Education spending, % of GDP	3.5
Doctors per 1,000 pop.	2.2	Enrolment, %: primary	100
Hospital beds per 1,000 pop.	14.3	secondary	101
Improved-water source access,		tertiary	57
% of pop.	100		

Society

No. of households	48.8m	Colour TVs per 100 households	99.5
Av. no. per household	2.6	Telephone lines per 100 pop.	43.0
Marriages per 1,000 pop.	5.5	Mobile telephone subscribers	
Divorces per 1,000 pop.	2.0	per 100 pop.	77.0
Cost of living, Dec. 2007		Computers per 100 pop.	67.6
New York = 100	125	Internet hosts per 1,000 pop.	287.1

a 2003

RUSSIA

Area	17,075,400 sq km	Capital	Moscow
Arable as % of total land	7	Currency	Rouble (Rb)

People

Population	142.5m	Life expectancy: men	59.0 yrs
Pop. per sq km	8.3	women	72.6 yrs
Av. ann. growth		Adult literacy	99.4%
in pop. 2010–15	-0.56%	Fertility rate (per woman)	1.4
Pop. under 15	15.1%	Urban population	73.3%
Pop. over 60	17.1%		per 1,000 pop.
No. of men per 100 women	86	Crude birth rate	10
Human Development Index	80.2	Crude death rate	16.2

The economy

GDP	Rb26,781bn	GDP per head	$6,930
GDP	$987bn	GDP per head in purchasing	
Av. ann. growth in real		power parity (USA=100)	29.8
GDP 1997–2007	6.3%	Economic freedom index	49.9

Origins of GDP

	% of total
Agriculture	4.9
Industry, of which:	39.3
manufacturing	19.4
Services	55.8

Components of GDP

	% of total
Private consumption	48.5
Public consumption	17.0
Investment	18.4
Exports	33.8
Imports	-21.1

Structure of employment

	% of total		% of labour force
Agriculture	10	Unemployed 2006	7.2
Industry	30	Av. ann. rate 1995–2006	9.6
Services	60		

Energy

	m TOE		
Total output	1,184.9	Net energy imports as %	
Total consumption	646.7	of energy use	-83
Consumption per head,			
kg oil equivalent	4,517		

Inflation and finance

Consumer price		av. ann. increase 2001–06	
inflation 2007	9.0%	Narrow money (M1)	36.5%
Av. ann. inflation 2002–07	11.2%	Broad money	36.5%
Money market rate, 2007	4.43%		

Exchange rates

	end 2007		December 2007
Rb per $	24.55	Effective rates	2000 = 100
Rb per SDR	38.79	– nominal	100.24
Rb per 7	36.14	– real	176.80

Trade

Principal exports		Principal imports	
	$bn fob		*$bn fob*
Fuels	196.8	Machinery & equipment	65.6
Metals	41.8	Food & drink	21.8
Machinery & equipment	17.5	Chemicals	21.6
Chemicals	16.9	Metals	9.6
Total incl. others	**303.6**	**Total incl. others**	**164.3**

Main export destinations		Main origins of imports	
	% of total		*% of total*
Netherlands	11.8	Germany	11.2
Italy	8.3	China	7.8
Germany	8.1	Ukraine	5.6
China	5.2	United States	3.9

Balance of payments, reserves and debt, $bn

Visible exports fob	303.9	Change in reserves	121.5
Visible imports fob	-164.7	Level of reserves	
Trade balance	139.2	end Dec.	303.8
Invisibles inflows	60.4	No. months of import cover	13.6
Invisibles outflows	-103.9	Official gold holdings, m oz	12.9
Net transfers	-1.5	Foreign debt	251.1
Current account balance	94.3	– as % of GDP	34
– as % of GDP	9.6	– as % of total exports	88
Capital balance	5.8	Debt service ratio	14
Overall balance	107.5		

Health and education

Health spending, % of GDP	5.2	Education spending, % of GDP	3.8
Doctors per 1,000 pop.	4.3	Enrolment, %: primary	96
Hospital beds per 1,000 pop.	9.7	secondary	84
Improved-water source access,		tertiary	72
% of pop.	97		

Society

No. of households	53.0m	Colour TVs per 100 households	93.9
Av. no. per household	2.7	Telephone lines per 100 pop.	30.8
Marriages per 1,000 pop.	7.6	Mobile telephone subscribers	
Divorces per 1,000 pop.	4.1	per 100 pop.	105.7
Cost of living, Dec. 2007		Computers per 100 pop.	12.2
New York = 100	107	Internet hosts per 1,000 pop.	25.1

SPAIN

Area	504,782 sq km	Capital	Madrid
Arable as % of total land	27	Currency	Euro (€)

People

Population	43.4m	Life expectancy: men	77.7 yrs
Pop. per sq km	86.0	women	84.2 yrs
Av. ann. growth		Adult literacy	...
in pop. 2010–15	0.39%	Fertility rate (per woman)	1.5
Pop. under 15	14.4%	Urban population	76.7%
Pop. over 60	21.7%		per 1,000 pop.
No. of men per 100 women	97	Crude birth rate	11
Human Development Index	94.9	Crude death rate	8.8

The economy

GDP	€976bn	GDP per head	$28,220
GDP	$1,225bn	GDP per head in purchasing	
Av. ann. growth in real		power parity (USA=100)	65.2
GDP 1997–2007	4.3%	Economic freedom index	69.7

Origins of GDP

	% of total	
Agriculture	3.7
Industry, of which:	30.4
manufacturing	...
Services	66.0

Components of GDP

	% of total
Private consumption	57.4
Public consumption	18.1
Investment	30.4
Exports	26.0
Imports	-32.2

Structure of employment

	% of total		% of labour force
Agriculture	5	Unemployed 2006	8.5
Industry	30	Av. ann. rate 1995–2006	15.0
Services	65		

Energy

	m TOE		
Total output	30.3	Net energy imports as %	
Total consumption	145.2	of energy use	79
Consumption per head,			
kg oil equivalent	3,346		

Inflation and finance

		av. ann. increase 2001–06	
Consumer price			
inflation 2007	2.8%	Euro area:	
Av. ann. inflation 2002–07	3.1%	Narrow money (M1)	10.5%
Money market rate, 2007	3.85%	Broad money	7.4%
		Household saving rate, 2007	10.3%

Exchange rates

	end 2007		December 2007
€ per $	0.68	Effective rates	2000 = 100
€ per SDR	1.07	– nominal	109.80
		– real	119.80

Trade

Principal exports		Principal imports	
	$bn fob		*$bn cif*
Raw materials &		Raw materials & intermediate	
intermediate products	104.6	products (excl. fuels)	145.0
Consumer goods	82.3	Consumer goods	88.8
Capital goods	21.6	Energy	49.8
		Capital goods	33.9
Total incl. others	**213.4**	Total incl. others	**326.1**

Main export destinations		Main origins of imports	
	% of total		*% of total*
France	18.7	Germany	14.2
Germany	10.9	France	12.8
Italy	8.8	Italy	8.2
EU25	70.9	EU25	58.8

Balance of payments, reserves and aid, $bn

Visible exports fob	216.5	Overall balance	0.6
Visible imports fob	-317.2	Change in reserves	2.1
Trade balance	-100.7	Level of reserves	
Invisibles inflows	155.4	end Dec.	19.3
Invisibles outflows	-153.9	No. months of import cover	0.5
Net transfers	-7.1	Official gold holdings, m oz	13.4
Current account balance	-106.3	Aid given	3.81
– as % of GDP	-8.7	– as % of GDP	0.31
Capital balance	110.4		

Health and education

Health spending, % of GDP	8.2	Education spending, % of GDP	4.2
Doctors per 1,000 pop.	3.1	Enrolment, %: primary	105
Hospital beds per 1,000 pop.	3.5	secondary	119
Improved-water source access,		tertiary	67
% of pop.	100		

Society

No. of households	15.3m	Colour TVs per 100 households	99.4
Av. no. per household	2.9	Telephone lines per 100 pop.	45.9
Marriages per 1,000 pop.	5.3	Mobile telephone subscribers	
Divorces per 1,000 pop.	1.7	per 100 pop.	106.4
Cost of living, Dec. 2007		Computers per 100 pop.	27.7
New York = 100	108	Internet hosts per 1,000 pop.	71.1

UNITED KINGDOM

Area	242,534 sq km	Capital	London
Arable as % of total land	24	Currency	Pound (£)

People

Population	59.8m	Life expectancy: men		77.2 yrs
Pop. per sq km	246.6	women		81.6 yrs
Av. ann. growth		Adult literacy		...
in pop. 2010–15	0.41%	Fertility rate (per woman)		1.9
Pop. under 15	18.0%	Urban population		89.2%
Pop. over 60	21.2%			per 1,000 pop.
No. of men per 100 women	96	Crude birth rate		12.0
Human Development Index	94.6	Crude death rate		9.9

The economy

GDP	£1,290bn	GDP per head	$39,750
GDP	$2,377bn	GDP per head in purchasing	
Av. ann. growth in real		power parity (USA=100)	75.3
GDP 1997–2007	3.2%	Economic freedom index	79.5

Origins of GDP		Components of GDP	
	% of total		% of total
Agriculture	0.9	Private consumption	63.2
Industry, of which:	24.0	Public consumption	21.7
manufacturing	...	Investment	18.2
Services	75.1	Exports	25.9
		Imports	-29.5

Structure of employment

	% of total		% of labour force
Agriculture	1	Unemployed 2005	5.0
Industry	22	Av. ann. rate 1995–2005	6.0
Services	77		

Energy

	m TOE		
Total output	204.3	Net energy imports as %	
Total consumption	233.7	of energy use	13
Consumption per head,			
kg oil equivalent	3,884		

Inflation and finance

Consumer price		av. ann. increase 2001–06	
inflation 2007	4.3%	Narrow money (M0)	5.6%
Av. ann. inflation 2002–07	3.2%	Broad money (M4)	9.7%
Money market rate, 2007	5.67%	Household saving rate, 2007	3.3%

Exchange rates

	end 2007		December 2007
£ per $	0.50	Effective rates	2000 = 100
£ per SDR	0.79	– nominal	98.80
£ per €	0.74	– real	104.70

Trade

Principal exports

	$bn fob
Finished manufactured products	251.8
Semi-manufactured products	119.9
Fuels	46.4
Food, drink & tobacco	20.4
Basic materials	9.0
Total incl. others	**448.3**

Principal imports

	$bn fob
Finished manufactured products	352.9
Semi-manufactured products	128.0
Fuels	58.4
Food, drink & tobacco	46.3
Basic materials	14.6
Total incl. others	**591.0**

Main export destinations

	% of total
United States	13.1
France	11.8
Germany	11.4
Ireland	7.2
Netherlands	6.8
EU25	62.8

Main origins of imports

	% of total
Germany	13.3
France	8.4
United States	8.0
Netherlands	7.0
Belgium-Luxembourg	5.7
EU25	58.2

Balance of payments, reserves and aid, $bn

Visible exports fob	449.5	Overall balance	-1.3
Visible imports fob	-592.4	Change in reserves	3.4
Trade balance	-142.9	Level of reserves	
Invisibles inflows	675.2	end Dec.	47.0
Invisibles outflows	-587.9	No. months of import cover	0.5
Net transfers	-22.0	Official gold holdings, m oz	10.0
Current account balance	-77.6	Aid given	12.46
– as % of GDP	-3.3	– as % of GDP	0.52
Capital balance	50.3		

Health and education

Health spending, % of GDP	8.2	Education spending, % of GDP	5.6
Doctors per 1,000 pop.	2.1	Enrolment, %: primary	105
Hospital beds per 1,000 pop.	3.9	secondary	98
Improved-water source access,		tertiary	59
% of pop.	100		

Society

No. of households	26.2m	Colour TVs per 100 households	99.5
Av. no. per household	2.3	Telephone lines per 100 pop.	56.2
Marriages per 1,000 pop.	5.2	Mobile telephone subscribers	
Divorces per 1,000 pop.	2.9	per 100 pop.	116.6
Cost of living, Dec. 2007		Computers per 100 pop.	75.8
New York = 100	139	Internet hosts per 1,000 pop.	129.2

UNITED STATES

Area	9,372,610 sq km	Capital	Washington DC
Arable as % of total land	19	Currency	US dollar ($)

People

Population	301.0m	Life expectancy: men		75.6 yrs
Pop. per sq km	32.1	women		80.8 yrs
Av. ann. growth		Adult literacy		...
in pop. 2010–15	0.89%	Fertility rate (per woman)		2.0
Pop. under 15	20.8%	Urban population		80.8%
Pop. over 60	16.6%		*per 1,000 pop.*	
No. of men per 100 women	97	Crude birth rate		14.0
Human Development Index	95.1	Crude death rate		8.2

The economy

GDP	$13,164bn	GDP per head	$43,730
Av. ann. growth in real		GDP per head in purchasing	
GDP 1997–2007	3.2%	power parity (USA=100)	100
		Economic freedom index	80.6

Origins of GDP		**Components of GDP**	
	% of total		*% of total*
Agriculture	0.9	Private consumption	69.9
Industry, of which:	20.9	Public consumption	19.1
manufacturing	12.6	Non-government investment	16.4
Services[a]	78.2	Exports	11.1
		Imports	-16.9

Structure of employment

	% of total		*% of labour force*
Agriculture	2	Unemployed 2006	4.6
Industry	20	Av. ann. rate 1995–2006	5.0
Services	78		

Energy

	m TOE		
Total output	1,630.7	Net energy imports as %	
Total consumption	2,340.3	of energy use	30
Consumption per head,			
kg oil equivalent	7,893		

Inflation and finance

Consumer price		*av. ann. increase 2001–06*	
inflation 2007	2.9%	Narrow money	1.3%
Av. ann. inflation 2002–07	2.9%	Broad money	5.7%
Treasury bill rate, 2007	4.41%	Household saving rate, 2007	0.7%

Exchange rates

	end 2007		*December 2007*
$ per SDR	1.58	Effective rates	*2000 = 100*
$ per €	1.47	– nominal	82.40
		– real	85.60

Trade

Principal exports	$bn fob	Principal imports	$bn fob
Capital goods, excl. vehicles	445.9	Industrial supplies	630.7
Industrial supplies	315.5	Consumer goods, excl. vehicles	474.9
Consumer goods, excl. vehicles	146.4	Capital goods, excl. vehicles	444.7
Vehicles & products	120.9	Vehicles & products	258.9
Food & beverages	84.2	Food & beverages	81.7
Total incl. others	**1,163.2**	Total incl. others	**1,953.3**

Main export destinations	% of total	Main origins of imports	% of total
Canada	21.4	China	16.5
Mexico	11.7	Canada	16.0
China	5.6	Mexico	10.8
Japan	5.4	Japan	7.4
Germany	4.3	Germany	4.8
United Kingdom	4.3	United Kingdom	2.9

Balance of payments, reserves and aid, $bn

Visible exports fob	1,026.9	Overall balance	-2.4
Visible imports fob	-1,861.4	Change in reserves	32.8
Trade balance	-834.6	Level of reserves	
Invisibles inflows	1,069.3	end Dec.	221.1
Invisibles outflows	-956.6	No. months of import cover	0.9
Net transfers	-89.6	Official gold holdings, m oz	261.5
Current account balance	-811.5	Aid given	23.53
– as % of GDP	-6.2	– as % of GDP	0.18
Capital balance	826.9		

Health and education

Health spending, % of GDP	15.9	Education spending, % of GDP	5.3
Doctors per 1,000 pop.	3.0	Enrolment, %: primary	98
Hospital beds per 1,000 pop.	3.3	secondary	94
Improved-water source access,		tertiary	82
% of pop.	100		

Society

No. of households	113.9m	Colour TVs per 100 households	98.5
Av. no. per household	2.6	Telephone lines per 100 pop.	57.2
Marriages per 1,000 pop.	7.6	Mobile telephone subscribers	
Divorces per 1,000 pop.	3.6	per 100 pop.	77.4
Cost of living, Dec. 2007		Computers per 100 pop.	76.2
New York = 100	100	Internet hosts per 1,000 pop.[b]	967.5

a Including utilities.
b Includes all hosts ending ".com", ".net" and ".org" which exaggerates the numbers.

All Economist books are available from
www.economistshop.com

Other Economist books include

Guide to Analysing
  Companies
Guide to Business Modelling
Guide to Business Planning
Guide to Economic Indicators
Guide to the European Union
Guide to Financial
  Management
Guide to Financial Markets
Guide to Investment Strategy
Guide to Management Ideas
  and Gurus
Guide to Organisation Design
Guide to Project Management
Numbers Guide
Style Guide

Book of Obituaries
Brands and Branding
Business Consulting
Business Strategy
Dealing with Financial Risk
Economics
Emerging Markets
Headhunters and How to Use
  Them
Mapping the Markets
Successful Strategy Execution
The City

Directors: an A–Z Guide
Economics: an A–Z Guide
Investment: an A–Z Guide
Negotiation: an A–Z Guide